Paley's Watchmaker

an abridged edition of
Wm Paley's
Natural Theology,
first published in 1802

Edited and introduced by
Bill Cooper

Foreword by
Dr Duane T. Gish

New Wine Press

New Wine Press
PO Box 17
Chichester
West Sussex PO20 6YB
England

ISBN: 1 874367 65 5

By the same author:
After the Flood (New Wine Press, 1995)

Typeset by CRB Associates, Reepham, Norfolk
Printed in England by Clays Ltd, St Ives plc.

Paley's Watchmaker

William Paley's *Natural Theology*, which was first published in 1802 and of which this present edition is an abridgement, is a phenomenon in the history of book publishing. Its impact was immediate and it ran through twenty editions in just its first eighteen years. Many more were to follow as, with his *Evidences of Christianity* (1794), it became required reading for every Cambridge undergraduate, and was to remain so right up to the 1920s. In short, it determined the course of learning at one of the world's leading universities for well over a hundred years, stemming the dual tides of evolutionism and atheism most effectively. Yet today, one can search for months on end and still be unable to find a copy. For all its numerous editions, it is one of the hardest books to obtain. Many reasons have been offered for this strange rarity, but I think the one most likely to be correct is that the work has always been prized too highly for people to easily part with it. No modern edition of the book exists, yet today Paley's brilliance and insight are needed as much as ever they were. Hence the appearance of this present abridgement.

for
Rebeccah and Lennie

Contents

Contents

Contents

Foreword

This edition of William Paley's *Natural Theology* is most timely and should be read with great interest and profit by those interested in the subject of origins. The contents of this book are just as valid today as they were when first issued nearly 200 years ago. In fact, in view of our greatly increased knowledge of the complexity of even a bacterial cell and of our recent awareness of the way in which the physical constants of the universe are so finely tuned for the existence of man, the views expressed by Paley are even more relevant today. This book by Paley, along with similar material contained in recent books, such as Michael Denton's *Evolution: A Theory in Crisis* and Michael Behe's *Darwin's Black Box – The Biochemical Challenge to Evolution* expose the piffle contained in Richard Dawkins' *The Blind Watchmaker*.

Anyone with an elementary knowledge of science should be able to discern the nonsense contained in Dawkins' example, for instance, of a computer program that converted a random arrangement of the letters contained in the sentence, 'Me thinks its like a weasel' into the right order. First, a human intelligence conceived the problem. Secondly, it required an incredibly complex computer. Thirdly, Dawkins programmed the computer to obtain the desired results. Fourthly, a goal had been established at the very beginning, but according to theory evolution has no goal and no idea where it is headed. Fifthly, even if one, two, three or more letters happen to be in the right place, the result is still gibberish and makes no more sense than the totally randomized mixture. Dawkins' exercise is pure sophomoric nonsense, but it appeals to many in the lay public who don't realize they have been hoodwinked. Sir Fred Hoyle was right when he said that the probability of a naturalistic evolutionary origin of life is equal to the probability that a tornado sweeping through a junkyard would assemble a Boeing 747.

The January 1980 issue of *Mechanical Engineering* contains an article (p. 28) by Professor D.H. Offner of the University of Illinois. In this article Professor Offner is urging his fellow engineers to consult living organisms for engineering designs that might prove helpful in their own attempts to solve problems. He refers to the pervasive nature of the evidence for design in the natural world and thus appears to give evidence of a designer. He states,

> 'Furthermore, since these products are found everywhere, appear to be interdependent, and indicate a design sophistication of a high order, a more descriptive title for this designer might be **G**rand **O**mni **D**esigner, easily remembered by the acronym, **GOD**.'

Yes, Sir Fred is right – Paley is in and Darwin is out.

We owe a debt of gratitude to the Creation Science Movement and Bill Cooper for this timely reissue of William Paley's *Natural Theology*.

Duane T. Gish
Senior Vice President
Institute for Creation Research
El Cajon, California

Introduction

'For the scientist who has lived by his faith in the power of reason, the story ends like a bad dream. He has scaled the mountain of ignorance; he is about to conquer the highest peak; [and] as he pulls himself over the final rock, he is greeted by a band of theologians who have been sitting there for centuries.'

(Robert Jastrow, Astrophysicist,
God and the Astronomers)

'It is ironic that the scientific facts throw Darwin out, but leave William Paley, a figure of fun to the scientific world for more than a century, still in the tournament ... with a chance of becoming the ultimate winner.'

(Sir Fred Hoyle, Astronomer,
Evolution from Space)

Few things are new under the sun, it seems, and today sees us as embroiled as ever in a controversy that has been raging now for more than two thousand years. Not just philosophers and scientists, but mankind in general seems to be divided up into two camps, two opposing and irreconcilable schools of thought. The issue boils down to this – there are those who contest that our universe was created, and those who contest that it wasn't. Both sides have summoned to their assistance a fearsome array of arguments and advocates over the years, but the chiefest of those arguments, and around which the battle has *always* raged, is that of 'evidence of design'. Does the universe display evidence which says that deliberate and caring thought has gone into its creation, or does it not? If it does, then it follows that that designing and caring thought can only have issued from a Mind which was necessarily greater than the universe it created. But if no such evidence is forthcoming, as some hold, then perhaps the universe has existed forever, or has come into being through accidental and entirely natural forces.

The battle has a fascinating history. As long ago as 44BC, the Stoic Cicero, arguably the most able advocate in law that ancient Rome had ever seen, and who knew a thing or two about examining conflicting testimony, pointed to evidence of design in the following way:

> 'When you see a sun-dial or a water-clock, you see that it tells the time by design and not by chance. How then can you imagine that the universe as a whole is devoid of purpose and intelligence when it embraces everything, including these artifacts themselves and their artificers? Our friend Posidonius as you know has recently made a globe which in its revolution shows the movements of the sun and stars and planets, by day and night, just as they appear in the sky. Now if someone were to take this globe and show it to the people of Britain or Scythia would a single one of those barbarians fail to see that it was the product of a conscious intelligence?' [1]

Lucretius, on the other hand, who lived during the same era as Cicero, and who embraced the Epicurean view, believed that all things had come into existence simply by the fortuitous and eternal jostling of atoms, arguing that any appearance of design was simply that, just appearance and nothing more.

The battle did not begin with Cicero and Lucretius, of course. It goes back much further than either of them,[2] but it is interesting to see Cicero using a time-piece for his analogy. The forbidding amount of design, thought and craftsmanship that has to go into the making of any time-piece, whether it be clockwork or water-driven, or uses the shadow of the sun, is evident in the extreme. So much so, in fact, that the analogy has been used with great success and passion even up to the present day. Except that recently a fresh attempt has been made to show that the analogy is erroneous.

In 1986, a book appeared whose title was *The Blind Watchmaker*. It was written by the evolutionist Richard Dawkins, who hoped to show in the book that all things had come into being through purely natural processes. It was a familiar argument, but to it Dawkins hoped to add a new twist by actually agreeing, in principle at any rate, with the creationist assertion that every watch must have a maker. However, he proposed that the 'watch', by which he meant the universe, had indeed come into existence through the work of a 'watchmaker', but a watchmaker which was blind, and not only blind but without intelligence or purpose – an unthinking and unconscious non-entity. It is otherwise known as natural selection.

Necessarily working at random, Dawkins' 'watchmaker' laboured on through millions of years, although to what end it could never know, until what was produced was a universe filled with an ingenuity and complexity that far surpasses that of any watch – a universe whose laws, parts and processes are today functioning with near perfection. Dawkins' argument, indeed the whole tenor of his book, was that it did not require an intelligent Creator to bring the universe, the earth and mankind into being. He argued instead that it was all a wonderful piece of good fortune, a watch made by nobody from a nothing that became unstable and went bang one day – a watch of inconceivable splendour whose design had required no designer, and in whose making no craftsman had a hand.

It was an attractively simplistic scheme which, it was hoped, would lend credibility to the theory of evolution – a theory which stands today in dire need of credibility. But alas for the notion, nothing is ever that simple, for standing in the way of Dawkins' scenario is a body of well established facts, facts of which scientists in the field have been aware for many years. Among them is the knowledge, confirmed by years of unbroken observation, that natural selection, where it works at all, can work only upon that which already exists. It can of itself create nothing new.

Moreover, genetic mutation, upon which all evolutionists must pin their hopes, and upon which natural selection works only by sifting it *out* of a population rather than putting it in, always results from a *loss* of information and organisation, and never a gain. Mutation leads only to damage and sterility within a species which already exists. Never can it work to the advantage of one that doesn't. Thus, mutations are seen to be a loss of complexity and order, and not the increase that evolution theory requires. Added to which, instead of being a creative principle, natural selection, which acts upon such mutations, is merely a safety mechanism that will resist, rather than encourage, change in an already established population. In other words, at best it is a conservative, occasionally a destructive, but certainly never a creative principle.

But though a great deal, that is not all, for there is much else that Dawkins' notion must ignore. For example, it takes no adequate account of recent discoveries in the realms of DNA and Information Theory, which are inexplicable if the origins of DNA are attributed merely to some primeval accident. This is because the extraordinary level of organised information which we find in the genetic code, can only have come, not from an unconscious, but from an intelligent and informative source. It is a fact that continues to surprise every scientist that works in the field, as does the sheer mind-boggling complexity of the subject. Professor Werner Gitt, for example, who is Head of Data Processing at the Federal Institute of Physics and Technology in Braunschweig, Germany, tells us that:

'The highest information density known to us is that of DNA molecules ... The storage capacity of DNA, the information carriers of living things, is 4.5×10^{13} times more effective than the megachip! ... The sum total of knowledge currently stored in the libraries of the world is estimated at 10^{18} bits. If this information could be stored in DNA molecules, 1% of the volume of a pinhead

18

would be sufficient for this purpose. If, on the other hand, this information were to be stored with the aid of megachips, we would need a pile higher than the distance between the earth and the moon.'[3]

The DNA molecule, of which even the simplest – some would say the most 'primitive' – forms of life are composed, is thus 45 million million times more efficient at holding and conveying information than the megachip. This is because the DNA molecule is an incredibly complex three-dimensional information storage system, where the megachip is only two-dimensional. But the DNA molecule's ability to store and convey such inconceivably large amounts of information so efficiently does not tell us where the information itself comes from. What is the source of that?

Information Theory, of which Professor Gitt is one of the world's leading exponents, is an important branch of scientific investigation which has shown conclusively and consistently that information cannot and does not arise from any state of non-information, just as life cannot proceed from non-life. Moreover, information has now come to be recognised as the Third Fundamental Quantity of the universe, which hitherto was thought to consist of merely two fundamental quantities, those of matter and energy. The DNA molecule is, of course, matter. Its activities are funded by energy. But the information that it carries is something else entirely. In other words, it is not sufficient to have only matter and energy for DNA to work. What is also required, at least to begin with, is a massive input of information for which matter and energy can give no account, and which neither of them can supply. Again, Professor Gitt tells us:

> 'According to Norbert Wiener, the founder of cyber-netics and information theory, information cannot be of a physical nature, even though it is transmitted by physical means: "Information is information, neither matter nor energy. No materialism that fails to take account of this can survive the present day." '[4]

But more discomforting still to the materialist, is not just the recent discovery of information to be the Third Fundamental Quantity, but rather the startling realisation of its source:

> 'If a basic code is found in any system, it can be concluded that the system originated from a mental concept, and did not arise by chance ... Meanings always represent mental concepts. They are distinct from matter and energy. They originate from an intelligent source. It is by means of language that information may be stored and transmitted on physical carriers. The information itself is entirely invariant ... The reason for this invariance lies in its non-material nature.'[5]

It would seem then that while some materialists have been busy looking in all the wrong places, certain physicists have stumbled upon the Mind of God. Information requires intelligence as its source, and intelligence requires mind. Which forces the conclusion that Dawkins' visually-challenged horologist must owe its existence to a source of great ignorance.

However, in coining the phrase 'blind watchmaker', Dawkins was not only attempting to add a new twist to an old controversy, but was paying grudging tribute to a thinker who had gone before him, William Paley, who, ironically, was arguing nearly two hundred years ago precisely the opposite to that which Dawkins now proposed. But according to Dawkins, and in spite of his tribute, 'Paley's argument is wrong, gloriously and utterly wrong.'[6]

The choice may have been unfortunate, however, for Paley, anticipating Dawkins on every point, had argued that it was just as ridiculous to assign the creation of the universe to chance as it was to say that a watch could also be made by chance. Thus, whoever Paley was arguing with at the time, and he does not name his antagonist, it obviously could not have been Dawkins. Which makes it all the more evident from everything Paley says, that Dawkins' arguments, though they be dressed in modern garb, are not only un-original, but are more than two hundred years out of date. So the twist which, it was hoped, would be added to the controversy, turns out to be not quite so new after all.

Whether Paley was gloriously wrong or not, may be judged by any reader of this present edition of his work. One molecular biologist today (though significantly not a creationist), happens to think he was right:

> 'Over the past twenty years Hume's criticism has been finally invalidated ... Paley was not only right in asserting the existence of an analogy between life and machines, but was also remarkably prophetic in guessing that the technological ingenuity in living systems is vastly in excess of anything yet accomplished by man.' [7]

Paley argues that the parts of a given watch are alone sufficient to persuade us that the watch must have had a maker who not only could *see* what he was doing, but who understood all the laws of physics that would govern the watch's operation, the laws of chemistry which would govern its composition, and the purpose and the end towards which it was made – the telling of time. And having proved the point by meeting every criterion of logic and common-sense, Paley then develops his analogy by bringing to our notice the evidences for design and purpose that are apparent in all living things, not least in ourselves and the extraordinarily complex bodies that we inhabit.

William Paley was born in 1743 into an age of philosophy, the so-called Age of Enlightenment, when more muddle-headed nonsense was written down than in any other age (our own excepted, perhaps). It was the age of Hume and Kant, of Thomas Paine and Erasmus Darwin – an age of scepticism, political revolution and religious turmoil, when the world's greatest minds, supposedly, endeavoured to build a brave new world, founded upon the supposition that God either did not exist or else that He was entirely ineffectual – a world which had somehow created itself and in which man was to be his own master. And the rationale upon which all this philosophy was built, was the supposition that as God did not exist or was blind, then all things must have come into being by chance. It was an erroneous supposition which Paley could not ignore, and he brought all his brilliance as a logician to bear upon it.

If there's one thing that makes Paley stand head and shoulders above his peers, it is his clear thinking – his incisive logic. This was recognised in his own day, in which he was acknowledged by all as a particularly brilliant mathematician. Mathematics requires above all else a tidy and a logical mind, and it was not for nothing that his own father, head of a local grammar school, once said of him that, 'he has by far the clearest head I ever met with in my life.'

Paley's lectures at Cambridge were delivered upon meta-physics, morals and the Greek New Testament, and his writings were prodigious, attacking such contemporary issues as the slave trade, and the taste that was rapidly becoming acquired amongst certain Englishmen of the day for political subversion and unrest. In 1794, his astonishingly successful *View of the Evidences of Christianity* appeared. It was a brilliant riposte to the scepticism of Hume and his colleagues, and it set Paley apart as a specially gifted apologist for the Christian faith. Indeed, from 1822 until 1920 his book was required reading for every Cambridge undergraduate. Then, just eight years after the publication of *Evidences*, appeared his *Natural Theology*, whose sub-title, *Evidence of the Existence and attributes of the Deity collected from the Appearances of Nature*, describes the book's contents exactly. First published in 1802, in the next eighteen years alone it was to pass through twenty editions, with many more to follow – in marked contrast to Hume's *Treatise of Human Nature*, which, Hume lamented, 'fell dead-born from the press!'

Paley's *Natural Theology* was to hold back the tide of evolutionism for more than fifty years after his death. And in a world that seemed literally hell-bent on throwing out the concept of its Creator, that was no mean achievement. Its arguments were, and still are, unanswerable except in the most strained and unlikely terms, and it is for this reason alone that the present edition of Paley has been issued. We may consider that in an age when men speak so glibly of 'blind watchmakers', then it is time for common-sense to enter the lists, and there is no better expression of common-sense in this field than that of Paley's book, which is here retitled *Paley's Watchmaker*.

Paley introduces us to a Watchmaker who could not only see what He was doing, but Who knows the beginning from the end, and Who demonstrates a wisdom and power that is truly awesome. Our author points out things that all of us take for granted about ourselves and the world around us, gently chiding us for too little appreciating not only the wisdom that has gone into our making, but also the love and care with which that wisdom has been applied. In short, having read Paley, it would be difficult to view the world or ourselves in quite the same light again.

What is very evident throughout the book is not only the author's encyclopaedic knowledge of his subject, but the child-like wonder that he displays as he views the natural world, and with which he brings forcefully to our attention the wisdom that has attended the smallest detail of its creation. And that child-like wonder is truly infectious. Paley has none of that arrogance that is the hall-mark of other philosophers. One has only to compare a chapter from Paley with one from Hegel, or Hobbes, or Hume, to see the difference that lies between them. Such men as these need a multitude of commentators to wrangle endlessly over the meaning of a subtle or ingenious phrase, or a sentiment not clearly expressed (and with which, indeed, they abound). But not Paley. He needs no commentary. The modern reader will experience no difficulty whatever in understanding all that Paley has to say, for he is meticulously clear in all his statements. All that remains, therefore, is for us to commend to the reader's attention the work that follows, with the hopeful prayer that it will make a difference.

Bill Cooper
Ashford, Middlesex
England
January 1997

Footnotes

1. Cicero. *De Natura Deorum.* (See *On the Nature of the Gods.* tr. Horace McGregor. 1988. Penguin Classics. Harmondsworth. p. 159).
2. Cooper, Bill. *After the Flood.* 1995. New Wine Press. Chichester. pp. 15–35. (Chapter 1: The knowledge of God amongst the early Pagans.)
3. CSM Pamphlet 276 – *Information: The Third Fundamental Quantity*, by Prof. Werner Gitt.
4. *ibid.*
5. *ibid.*
6. Dawkins, R. *The Blind Watchmaker.* 1986.
7. Denton, Michael. *Evolution: A Theory in Crisis.* 1985.

Editor's Notes

To bring this present edition to the modern reader has required merely the updating of the original punctuation and the omission of repetitious or superfluous material. Otherwise the work is entirely Paley's own. The magnificent English that Paley employs is straight out of the 18th-century, and has the satisfying virtue of being readily understood by today's reader. Occasionally, however, it has been necessary to insert a word here and there so that a given or an edited sentence can make better sense. These occasions are rare, and are always marked with square parentheses []. All round parentheses ( ) are Paley's own. The phraseology, of course, is dated, as are certain technical terms that Paley employs. But I have left them as they are. To alter them, or to update them, would have spoiled the flow of the argument. The chapter divisions, but especially the paragraphs, are half Paley's, half my own.

Bill Cooper

Paley's
Watchmaker

Chapter One

In crossing a heath, suppose I pitched my foot against a stone, and were asked how the stone came to be there. I might possibly answer that for anything I knew to the contrary it had lain there forever. Nor would it perhaps be very easy to show the absurdity of this answer. But suppose I had found a *watch* upon the ground, and it should be inquired how the watch happened to be in that place. I should hardly think of the answer which I had before given, that for anything I knew the watch might have always been there. Yet why should not this answer serve for the watch as well as for the stone? Why is it not as admissible in the second case as in the first? For this reason and for no other – that when we come to inspect the watch, we perceive (what we could not discover in the stone) that its several parts are framed and put together for a purpose, that they are so formed and adjusted as to produce motion, and that motion so regulated as to point out the hour of the day. That if the different parts had been differently shaped from what they are, or placed in any other order than that in which they are placed, either no motion at all would have been carried on in the machine, or none which would have answered the use that is now served by it.

To reckon up a few of the plainest of these parts, we see a cylindrical box containing a coiled spring, which by its endeavour to relax itself turns the box. We next observe a flexible chain (artificially wrought for the sake of flexure) communicating the action of the spring from the box to the fusee. We then find a series of wheels, the teeth of which catch in and apply to each other, conducting the motion from the fusee to the balance and from the balance to the pointer. We notice that the wheels are made of brass in order to keep them from rust, [and that] the springs [are made] of steel, no other metal being so elastic; that over the face of the watch there is placed a glass, a material employed in no other part of the work, but in the room of which, if there had been any other than a transparent substance, the hour could not be seen. This mechanism being observed, the inference is inevitable that the watch must have had a maker, [and] that there must have existed an artificer who formed it for the purpose which we find it to answer, who comprehended its construction and designed its use.

Nor would it weaken the conclusion that we had never seen a watch made, that we had never known an artist capable of making one, that we were altogether incapable of executing such a piece of workmanship ourselves, or of understanding in what manner it was performed – all this being true of ancient art, of some lost arts, and of the curious productions of modern manufacture. Does one man in a million know how oval frames are turned? Ignorance of this kind exalts our opinion of the unseen and unknown artist's skill, if he be unseen and unknown, but raises no doubt in our minds of the existence and agency of such an artist. Nor can I perceive that it varies the inference whether the question arise concerning a human agent or an agent possessing a different nature.

Neither would it invalidate our conclusion that the watch sometimes went wrong, or that it seldom went exactly right. The purpose of the machinery, the design and the designer, would be evident whether we could account for it or not. It is not necessary that a machine be perfect in order to show with what design it was made, [and] still less necessary where the only question is whether it were made with any design at all. Nor would it bring any uncertainty into the argument if there were a few parts of the watch we had not yet discovered. Nor would any man in his senses think the existence of the watch accounted for by being told that it was one out of [many] possible combinations of material forms, nor that there existed in things a principle of order which had disposed the parts of the watch into their present form and situation. He never knew a watch made by the principle of order. Nor can he even form to himself an idea of what is meant by a principle of order [as] distinct from the intelligence of the watch-maker. He would be surprised to hear that the mechanism of the watch was no proof of contrivance [but] only a motive to induce the mind to think so. And not less surprised to be informed that the watch in his hand was nothing more that the result of the laws of metallic nature.

It is a perversion of language to assign any law as the efficient operative cause of anything. A law presupposes an agent, for it is only the mode according to which an agent proceeds. It implies a power, for it is the order according to which that power acts. Without this agent, without this power, which are both distinct from itself, the law does nothing [and] is nothing. The expression 'the law of metallic nature' may sound strange and harsh to a philosophic ear, but it seems quite as justifiable as some others which are more familiar to him, such as the 'law of vegetable nature', the 'law of animal nature', or indeed as the 'law of nature' in general when assigned as the cause of phenomena in exclusion of agency and power.

Neither, lastly, would our observer be driven out of his conclusion or from his confidence in its truth, by being told that he knew nothing at all about the matter. He knows enough for his argument. He knows the utility of the end. He knows the subserviency and adaptation of the means to the end. These points being known, his ignorance of other points affect not the certainty of his reasoning. The consciousness of knowing little need not beget a distrust of that which he does know.

Chapter Two

Suppose in the next place that the person who found the watch should discover that, in addition to all the properties which he had hitherto observed in it, it possessed the unexpected property of producing another watch like itself! That it contained within it a mechanism, a system of parts, evidently and separately calculated for this purpose. Let us inquire what effect ought such a discovery to have upon his former conclusion.

The first effect would be to increase his admiration of the contrivance and the consummate skill of the contriver. Whether he regarded the apparatus, the intricate yet in many parts intelligible mechanism by which it was carried on, he would perceive in this new observation nothing but an additional reason for doing what he had already done – referring the construction of the watch to design and to supreme art! If that construction *without* this property proved intention of art to have been employed about it, still more strong would the proof appear when he came to the knowledge of this further property, the crown and perfection of all the rest!

He would reflect that though the watch before him were *in some sense* the maker of the watch which was fabricated in the course of its movements, yet it was in a very different sense from that in which a carpenter, for instance, is the maker of a chair. In no sense was it the author of the constitution and order of the parts which the new watch contained, or of the parts by which it was produced. We might possibly say with great latitude of expression that a stream of water ground corn. But no latitude of expression would allow us to say that the stream of water built the mill, though it were too ancient for us to know who the builder was. What the stream of water does in the affair is neither more nor less than this: by the application of an unintelligent impulse to a mechanism previously arranged, and arranged by an intelligence, an effect is produced. The corn is ground. But the effect results from the arrangement. The force of the stream cannot be said to be the cause or author of the effect, still less of the arrangement. Understanding and plan in the formation of the mill were not the less necessary for any share which the water has in grinding the corn. Yet this share is the same as that which the watch would have contributed to the production of the new watch.

Therefore, though it be now no longer probable that the watch which our observer had found was made *immediately* by the hand of an artificer, yet doth not this in any wise affect the inference that an artificer had been originally employed and concerned in the production. The argument from design remains. There cannot be design without a designer, a contrivance without a contriver, order without choice, arrangement without anything capable of arranging, purpose without that which could intend a purpose, means suitable to an end without the end ever having been contemplated or the means accomodated to it. Arrangement, disposition of parts, subserviency of means to an end, [and] relation of instruments to a use, imply the presence of intelligence and mind.

No one therefore can rationally believe that the insensible, inanimate watch from which the watch before us issued, was the proper cause of the mechanism we so much admire in it, [or] could be truly said to have constructed the instrument, disposed its parts, assigned their office, determined their order, action and mutual dependency, [or] combined their several motions into one result.

Nor is anything gained by running the difficulty farther back by supposing the watch before us to have been produced from another watch, that from a former, and so on indefinitely. Our going back ever so far brings us no nearer to the least degree of satisfaction upon the subject. Contrivance is still unaccounted for. We still want a contriver. A designing mind is neither supplied by this supposition nor dispensed with. If the difficulty were diminished the farther we went back, by going back indefinitely we might exhaust it – and this is the only case to which this sort of reasoning applies! Nothing is effected by lengthening the series. A chain composed of an infinite number of links can no more support itself than a chain composed of a finite number of links. And of this we are assured because by increasing the number of links from ten to a hundred, [and] from a hundred to a thousand, we observe not the smallest tendency towards self-support. There is no difference in this respect between a chain that is finite and one that is infinite.

This very much resembles the case before us. The machine which we are inspecting demonstrates, by its construction, [both] contrivance and design. Contrivance must have had a contriver, [and] design a designer, whether the machine immediately proceeded from another machine or not. That machine *may* have proceeded from another machine. Nor does that alter the case. A contriver is still necessary. And the question which irresistibly presses upon our thoughts is: Whence [comes] this contrivance and design? The thing required is the intending mind, the adapting hand, [and] the intelligence by which that hand was directed. This question is not shaken off by increasing a number or succession of these properties, nor the more by increasing that number to infinity. It is in vain therefore to assign a series of such causes or to allege that a series may be carried back to infinity. For here is contrivance, but no contriver. Proofs of design, but no designer. Can this be maintained without absurdity? Yet this is atheism.

Chapter Three

This is atheism, for every indication of contrivance, every manifestation of design which existed in the watch, exists in the works of nature, with the difference on the side of nature of being greater in a degree which exceeds all computation. I mean that the contrivances of nature surpass the contrivances of art in the complexity, subtlety and curiosity of the mechanism. And still more, if possible, do they go beyond them in number and variety, yet in a multitude of cases are not less evidently mechanical, not less evidently contrivances, not less evidently accommodated to their end or suited to their office, than are the most perfect productions of human ingenuity.

I know of no better method of introducing so large a subject than that of comparing a single thing with a single thing: an eye, for example, with a telescope. As far as the examination of the instrument goes, there is precisely the same proof that the eye was made for vision as there is that the telescope was made for assisting it! They are made upon the same principles, both being adjusted to the laws by which the transmission and refraction of rays of light are regulated. I speak not of the origin of the laws themselves, but such laws being fixed the construction in both cases is adapted to them. For instance, these laws require, in order to produce the same effect, that the rays of light in passing from water into the eye, should be refracted by a more convex surface than when it passes out of air into the eye. Accordingly, we find that the eye of a fish, in that part of it called the crystalline lens, is much rounder than the eye of terrestrial animals. What plainer manifestation of design can there be than this difference? What could a mathematical-instrument-maker have done more to show his knowledge of his principle, his application of that knowledge, [or] his suiting of his means to his end?

To some it may appear a difference sufficient to destroy all similitude between the eye and the telescope that the one is a perceiving organ, [and] the other an unperceiving instrument. The fact is that they are both instruments. And, as to the mechanism, this varies not the analogy at all. For observe what the constitution of the eye is. It is necessary in order to produce distinct vision, that an image or picture of the object be formed at the bottom of the eye. Whence this necessity arises, or how the picture is connected with the sensation, or contributes to it, we will confess impossible for us to search out. [But] it is a matter of certainty, because it is a matter which experience and observation demonstrate, that the formation of an image at the bottom of the eye is necessary to perfect vision. The image itself can be shown. Whatever affects the distinctness of the image, affects the distinctness of the vision. The formation then of such an image being necessary (no matter how) to the sense of sight and to the exercise of that sense, the apparatus by which it is formed is constructed and put together not only with infinitely more art, but upon the self-same principles of art as in the telescope.

The perception arising from the image may be laid out of the question. For the production of the image, these are instruments of the same kind. The end is the same. The means are the same. The purpose in both is alike. The contrivance for accomplishing that purpose is in both alike. The lenses of the telescope and of the eye bear a complete resemblance to one another in their figure, their position, and in their power over the rays of light in bringing each pencil [of light] to a point at the right distance from the lens, namely in the eye at the exact place where the membrane is spread to receive it. How is it possible under circumstances of such close affinity, and under the operation of equal evidence, to exclude contrivance from the one, yet to acknowledge the proof of contrivance having been employed as the plainest and clearest of all propositions in the other?

The resemblance between the two cases is still more accurate, and obtains in more points, than we are aware of. In dioptric telescopes there is an imperfection. Pencils of light, in passing through glass lenses, are separated into different colours, thereby tinging the object, especially the edges of it, as if it were viewed through a prism. To correct this inconvenience has long been a desideratum in the art. At last it came into the mind of a sagacious optician to inquire how this matter was managed in the eye, in which there was exactly the same difficulty to contend with as in the telescope. His observation taught him that in the eye the [problem] was cured by combining lenses of different substances which possessed different refracting powers. Our artist borrowed thence his hint and produced a correction of the defect by imitating, in glasses made from different materials, the effects of the different humours through which the rays of light pass before they reach the bottom of the eye. Could this be in the eye without purpose which suggested to the optician the only effectual means of attaining that purpose?

But further, there are other points not so much perhaps of strict resemblance between the two, as of [the] superiority of the eye over the telescope. Two things were wanted to the eye which were not wanted (at least in the same degree) to the telescope, and these were the adaptation of the organ to different degrees of light, and to the vast diversity of distance at which objects are viewed by the naked eye – from a few inches to as many miles! These difficulties present not themselves to the maker of the telescope. He wants all the light he can get, and he never directs his instrument to objects near at hand. In the eye, both these cases were to be provided for, and for the purpose of providing for them a subtle and appropriate mechanism is introduced.

In order to exclude excess of light, and to render objects visible under obscurer degrees of it, the hole or aperture in the eye through which the light enters, is so formed as to contract or dilate itself for the purpose of admitting a greater or less number of rays at the same time. The chamber of the eye is a camera-obscura which, when the light is too small, can enlarge its opening, [and] when too strong can again retract it. It is also to be observed that this hole in the eye, which we call the pupil, under all its different dimensions, retains its exact circular shape. Let an artist only try to execute the same. He will find that his threads and strings must be disposed with great consideration and contrivance to make a circle which shall continually change its diameter yet preserve its form!

The second difficulty which has been stated was the suiting of the same organ to the perception of objects that lie near at hand within a few inches, and of objects which are placed at a considerable distance from it – of as many furlongs! Now this, according to the principles of optics (and these laws are fixed) could not be done without the organ itself undergoing an alteration and receiving an adjustment that might correspond with the rays of light [which] reached it. Rays issuing from points placed at a small distance from the eye, and which consequently must enter the eye in spreading or diverging order, cannot by the same optical instrument in the same state be brought to a point, [or] be made to form an image, with rays proceeding from objects situated at a much greater distance, and which arrive at the eye in directions nearly parallel. It requires a rounder lens to do it. The point of concourse behind the lens must fall critically upon the retina, or the vision is confused. Yet, other things remaining the same, this point, by the immutable properties of light, is carried farther back when the rays proceed from a near object than when they are sent from one that is remote. A person who was using an optical instrument would manage this matter by changing, as occasion required, his lens or his telescope, or by adjusting the distance of his glass with his hand. But how is it to be managed in the eye?

What the alteration was had long formed a subject of inquiry and conjecture, [for] the change, though sufficient for the purpose, is so minute as to elude ordinary observation. [However], some very late discoveries seem at length to have ascertained the mechanical alteration which the parts of the eye undergo. It is found that, by the action of certain muscles, whenever the eye is directed to a near object, three changes are produced in it at the same time, all severally contributing to the adjustment required. The cornea, or outermost coat of the eye, is rendered more round and prominent. The crystalline lens underneath is pushed forward, and the axis of vision (as the depth of the eye is called) is elongated! These changes in the eye vary its power over the rays of light in such a manner and degree as to produce exactly the effect which is wanted, the formation of an image upon the retina.

Can anything be more decisive of contrivance than this? The most secret laws of optics must have been known to the author of a structure endowed with such a capacity of change. It is as though an optician, when he had a nearer object to view, should rectify his instrument by putting in another glass, at the same time drawing out his tube to a different length!

Observe a new-born child first lifting up its eyelids. What does the opening of the curtain discover? The anterior part of two pellucid globes which, when they come to be examined, are found to be constructed upon strict optical principles – the self-same principles upon which we ourselves construct optical instruments! We find them perfect for the purpose of forming an image by refraction, composed of parts executing different offices, one part having fulfilled its office upon the pencil of light, delivering it over to the action of another part, that to a third, and so onward, the progressive action depending for its success upon the nicest and minutest adjustment of the parts concerned. Yet, these parts [are] so in fact adjusted as to produce, not by a simple action or effect but by a combination of actions and effects, the result which is ultimately wanted.

And forasmuch as this organ would have to operate under different circumstances, with strong light and with weak, upon near objects and remote ones, we find its several parts capable of being changed and a most artificial apparatus provided to produce that change! This is far beyond the common regulator of a watch, which requires the touch of a foreign hand to set it. But it is not altogether unlike Harrison's contrivance for making a watch regulate itself by the artful use of the different expansion of metals. The ingenuity of this last contrivance has been justly praised. Shall therefore a structure which differs from it chiefly by surpassing it, be accounted no contrivance at all? Or if it be a contrivance, that it is without a contriver?

But this, though much, is not the whole. Birds, for instance, procure their food by means of their beak, and the distance between the eye and the point of the beak being small, it becomes necessary that they should have the power of seeing very near objects distinctly. On the other hand, from being often elevated above the ground, living in the air and moving through it with great velocity, they require for their safety as well as for their prey, a power of seeing at a great distance – a power of which surprising examples are given! Two peculiarities are found in the eyes of birds, both tending to facilitate the change upon which the adjustment of the eye to different distances depends. The one is a bony, yet in most species a flexible rim or hoop surrounding the broadest part of the eye, which, confining the action of the muscles to that part, increases the effect of their lateral pressure upon the orb, by which pressure its axis is elongated for the purpose of looking at very near objects. The other is an additional muscle called the marsupium, to draw the crystalline lens back and to fit the same eye for the viewing of very distant objects. By these means, the eyes of birds can pass from one extreme to another of their scale of adjustment with more ease and readiness than the eyes of other animals.

The eyes of fishes also exhibit certain distinctions of structure adapted to their state and element. We have already observed the figure of the crystalline [lens] compensating by its roundness the density of the medium through which their light passes. To which we have to add that the eyes of fish, in their natural and indolent state, appear to be adjusted to near objects, in this respect differing from the human eye as well as those of quadrupeds and birds. The ordinary shape of a fish's eye being in a much higher degree convex than that of land animals, a corresponding difference attends its muscular conformation – that it is throughout calculated for *flattening* the eye!

The iris also, in fish, does not admit of contraction. This is a great difference, of which the probable reason is that the diminished light in water is never too strong for the retina!

In the eel, which has to work its head through sand and gravel, the roughest and harshest substances, there is placed before the eye, and at some distance from it, a transparent, horny, convex case or covering which, without obstructing the sight, defends the organ. To such an animal, could anything be more wanted or more useful?

Thus, in comparing the eyes of different kinds of animals, we see in their resemblances and distinctions one general plan laid down, and that plan varied with the varying exigencies to which it is to be applied. There is one property, however, common I believe to all eyes, at least to all which have been examined, that the optic nerve enters the bottom of the eye not in the centre or middle, but a little on one side, not in the point where the axis of the eye meets the retina, but between that point and the nose. The difference which this makes is that no part of an object is unperceived by both eyes at the same time.

In considering vision as achieved by the means of an image formed at the bottom of the eye, we can never reflect without wonder upon the smallness, yet correctness, of the picture, the subtlety of the touch [or] the fineness of the lines. A landscape of five or six square leagues is brought into a space of half an inch diameter. Yet the multitude of objects which it contains are all preserved, are all discriminated in their magnitudes, positions, figures [and] colours. The prospect from Hampstead Hill is compressed into the compass of a six-pence, yet circumstantially represented. A stage coach travelling at its ordinary speed for half an hour passes, in the eye, only over one twelfth of an inch, yet this change of place in the image [is] distinctly perceived throughout its whole progress, for it is only by means of that perception that the motion of the coach itself is made sensible to the eye. If anything can abate our admiration of the smallness of the visual tablet compared with the extent of vision, it is a reflection which the view of nature leads us every hour to make – that, in the hands of the Creator, great and little are nothing!

Sturmius held that the examination of the eye was a cure for atheism, [for] besides that conformity to optical principles which its internal constitution displays, and which amounts to a manifestation of intelligence in the structure, there is to be seen in everything belonging to it and about it an extra-ordinary degree of care, an anxiety for its preservation, due, if we may so speak, to its value and its tenderness. It is lodged in a strong, deep, bony socket composed by the junction of seven bones hollowed out at their edges. In some species, as that of the coatimondi, the orbit is not bony throughout. But wherever this is the case, the upper, which is the deficient part, is supplied by a cartilaginous ligament, a substitution which shows the same care. Within this socket it is imbedded in fat, of all animal substances the best adapted both to its repose and motion.

But of the superficial parts of the animal frame, I know none which, in its office and structure, is more deserving of attention than the eyelid. It defends the eye. It wipes it. It closes it in sleep. Are there, in any work of art whatever, purposes more evident than those which this organ fulfils? Or an apparatus for executing those purposes more intelligible, more appropriate, or more mechanical?

We have made a choice of the eye as an instance upon which to rest the argument of this chapter. Some single example was to be proposed, and the eye offered itself under the advantage of admitting a strict comparison with optical instruments. The ear, it is probable, is no less artificially and mechanically adapted to its office than the eye, but we know less about it. We do not so well understand the action, the use, or the mutual dependency of its internal parts. Its general form, however, both external and internal, is sufficient to show that it is an instrument adapted to the reception of sound. That is to say, already knowing that sound consists in pulses of the air, we perceive in the structure of the ear a suitableness to receive impressions from this, and to propagate the impressions to the brain. For of what does this structure consist?

An external ear (the concha), calculated, like an ear-trumpet, to catch and collect the pulses of which we have

spoken, in large quadrupeds turning to the sound and possessing a configuration as well as motion evidently fitted for the
office. A tube which leads into the head. A thin membrane. A
chain of moveable and infinitely curious bones. Cavities,
similar in shape to wind instruments, being spiral or portions
of circles, [and] the eustachian tube. This assemblage of
connected parts constitutes together an apparatus plainly
enough relative to the transmission of sound, only to be
lamented in not being better understood.

The communication within, formed by the small bones of
the ear, is, to look upon, more like what we are accustomed to
call machinery than anything I am acquainted with in animal
bodies. It seems evidently designed to continue, towards
the sensorium, the tremulous motions which are excited
in the membrane of the tympanum, or what is better known
by the name of the 'drum of the ear'. The compages of bones
consists of four, which are so disposed and so hinged upon one
another that if the membrane, the drum of the ear, vibrate, all
four [bones] are put in motion together, and, by the result of
their action, work the base of that [bone] which is last in the
series upon an aperture which it closes, and which aperture
opens into the tortuous canals that lead to the brain.

This last bone of the four is called the stapes. The office of
the drum of the ear is to spread out an extended surface
capable of receiving sound, and of being put into a state of
vibration. The office of the stapes is to repeat these vibrations.
From which account of its action may be understood how the
use of the chain of bones is to propagate the impulse in a
direction towards the brain, and to propagate it with the
advantage of a lever. Which advantage consists of increasing
the force and strength of the vibration, and at the same time
diminishing the space through which it oscillates – both of
which changes augment or facilitate the still deeper action
of the auditory nerves!

The benefit of the eustachian tube may be made out upon
known pneumatic principles. Behind the drum of the ear is
a second cavity called the tympanum. The eustachian tube is a
pipe sufficient for the passage of air, leading from this cavity

into the back part of the mouth. Now, it would not have done to have had a vacuum in this cavity, for in that case the pressure of the atmosphere from without, would have burst the membrane which covered it. Nor would it have done to have filled the cavity with lymph or any other secretion, which would necessarily have obstructed both the vibration of the membrane and the play of the small bones. Nor, lastly, would it have done to have occupied the space with confined air, because the expansion of that air by heat, or its contraction by cold, would have distended or relaxed the covering membrane in a degree inconsistent with the purpose which it was assigned to execute. The only remaining expedient the eustachian tube serves, [which] is to open to this cavity a communication with the external air. In one word, it exactly answers the purpose of the hole in a drum.

The membrana tympani likewise deserves all the examination which can be made of it. It is not found in the ears of fish, which furnishes an additional proof that it is appropriated to the action of air. It bears an obvious resemblance to the pelt or head of a drum from which it takes its name. It resembles also a drum-head in this principal property, that its use depends upon its tension. Tension is the state essential to it. Now we know that in a drum the pelt is carried over a hoop and braced as occasion requires by the means of strings attached to its circumference. In the membrane of the ear the same purpose is provided for, more simply but not less mechanically, nor less successfully, by a different expedient – by the end of a bone (the handle of the malleus) pressing upon its centre!

It is only in very large animals that the texture of this membrane can be discerned. In the *Philosophical Transactions* for the year 1800 (vol. i.), Mr Everard Home has given some curious observations upon the ear, and the drum of the ear, of an elephant. He discovered in it what he calls a radiated muscle, that is straight muscular fibres, passing along the membrane from the circumference to the centre, from the bony rim which surrounds it towards the handle of the malleus to which the central part is attached. This muscle he supposes to be designed to bring the membrane into unison with different sounds. But then he also discovered that this muscle itself cannot act unless the membrane be drawn to a stretch and kept in a due state of tightness by what may be called a foreign force – the action of the muscles of the malleus! Supposing his explanation of the use of the parts to be just, our author is well founded in the reflection which he makes upon it: 'that this mode of adapting the ear to different sounds, is one of the most beautiful applications of muscles in the body; the mechanism is so simple, and the variety of effects so great.'

In another volume of the *Transactions* above referred to, and of the same year, two most curious cases are related of persons who retained the sense of hearing, not in a perfect but in a very considerable degree, notwithstanding the almost total loss of the membrane we have been describing. In one of these cases, the use here assigned to that membrane of modifying the impressions of sound by change of tension, was attempted to be supplied by straining the muscles of the outward ear! 'The external ear,' we are told, 'had acquired a distinct motion upward and backward, which was observable whenever the patient listened to anything which he did not distinctly hear. When he was addressed in a whisper, the ear was seen immediately to move. When the tone of voice was louder, it then remained altogether motionless.'

It appears probable from both these cases that a collateral, if not principal use of the membrane, is to cover and protect the barrel of the ear which lies behind it. Both the patients suffered from cold, one [suffering] 'a great increase of deafness from catching cold,' the other 'very considerable pain from exposure to a stream of cold air.' Bad effects therefore followed from this cavity being left open to the external air. Yet, had the Author of nature shut it up by any other cover than what was capable of receiving sound, the use of the organ, so far as we can judge, must have been entirely obstructed!

Chapter Four

The generation of the animal no more accounts for the contrivance of the eye or ear than upon the supposition stated in a preceding chapter, the production of a watch by the motion and mechanism of a former watch. I do insist most strenuously upon the correctness of this comparison. It holds as to every mode of propagation. Whatever was true of the watch, is true of plants and animals.

To begin with the fructification of plants. Can it be doubted but that the seed contains a particular organization? Whether latent, or whatever else it be, it encloses an organization suited to the germination of a new plant. Has the plant which produced the seed anything more to do with that organization than the watch would have? Has it anything at all to do with the *contrivance* [of it]? The maker and contriver of one watch, when he inserted within it a mechanism suited to the production of another watch, was in truth the maker and contriver of that other watch. All the properties of the new watch were to be referred to his agency, the design manifested in it to his intention, the art to him as the artist, the collocation of each part to his placing, the action, effect and use to his counsel, intelligence and workmanship. In producing it by the intervention of a former watch, he was only working by one set of tools instead of another. So it is with the plant and the seed produced by it. Can any distinction be assigned between the cases, between the producing watch and producing plant, both [of them] passive, unconscious substances? [Or] by the organization which was given to them producing their like, without understanding or design – both, that is, instruments?

From plants we may proceed to oviparous animals, from seeds to eggs. Now I say that the bird has the same concern in the formation of the egg which she lays as the plant has in that of the seed. No other, nor greater. The internal constitution of the egg is as much a secret to the hen as if the hen were inanimate. Her will cannot alter it or change a single feather of the chick. She can neither foresee nor determine of which sex her brood shall be, or how many of either. If there be concealed within that smooth shell a provision and a preparation for the production and nourishment of a new animal, they are not of her providing or preparing. If there be contrivance, it be none of hers.

Although therefore there be the difference of life and perceptivity between the animal and the plant, it is a difference which enters not into the account. The animal function and the vegetable function are alike destitute of any design which can operate upon the form of the thing produced. The plant has no design in producing the seed, [and] no comprehension of the nature or use of what it produces. The bird, with respect to the egg, is not above the plant with respect to its seed. Neither the one nor the other bears that sort of relation to what proceeds from them which a joiner does to the chair which he makes. Now, a cause which bears *this* relation to the effect is what we want in order to account for the suitableness of [the] means to an end, the fitness or fitting of one thing to another. And this cause the parent plant or animal does not supply!

It is further observable concerning the propagation of plants and animals, that the apparatus employed exhibits no resemblance to the thing produced, in this respect holding an analogy with instruments and tools of art. The filaments, antherae and stigmata of flowers bear no more resemblance to the young plant, or even to the seed, which is formed by their intervention than a chisel or a plane does to a table or chair. What then are the filaments, antherae and stigmata of plants but instruments strictly so called?

We may advance from animals which bring forth eggs to animals which bring forth their young alive, and of this latter class from the highest to the lowest, from irrational to rational life, from brutes to the human species, without perceiving as we proceed any alteration whatever in the terms of the comparison. The rational animal does not produce its offspring with more certainty or success than the irrational animal, a man than a quadruped, a quadruped than a bird, nor (for we may follow the gradation through its whole scale) a bird than a plant, nor a plant than a watch, a piece of dead mechanism. Rationality, therefore, has nothing to do in the business.

If an account must be given of the contrivance which we observe, if it be demanded whence arose either the contrivance by which the young animal is produced or the contrivance manifested in the young animal itself, it is not from the reason of the parent that any such account can be drawn. He is the cause of his offspring in the same sense in which a gardener is the cause of the tulip. We admire the flower, we examine the plant, we perceive the conduciveness of many of its parts to their end and office. We observe a provision for its nourishment, growth, protection and fecundity. But we never think of the gardener in all this! We attribute nothing to his agency, yet it may still be true that without the gardener we should not have had the tulip. Just so it is with the succession of animals, even of the highest order.

For the contrivance discovered in the structure of the thing produced, we want a contriver. The parent is not the contriver. He is in total ignorance why that which is produced took its present form rather than any other. It is for him only to be astonished by the effect. We can no more look, therefore, to the intelligence of the parent animal for what we are in search of, than refer the internal conformation of an acorn to the intelligence of the oak from which it dropped, or the structure of the watch to the intelligence of the watch which produced it – there being no difference as far as [this] argument is concerned between an intelligence which is not exerted and an intelligence which does not exist!

Chapter Five

When we are inquiring simply after the *existence* of an intelligent Creator, imperfection, inaccuracy, liability to disorder [and] occasional irregularities may subsist in a considerable degree without inducing any doubt into the question. Just as a watch may frequently go wrong, seldom perhaps exactly right [or] may be faulty in some parts, without the smallest ground of suspicion from thence arising that it was not a watch, or [was] not made for the purpose ascribed to it. But, after all, these are different questions from the question of the artist's existence. So likewise it is in the works of nature. Irregularities and imperfections are of little or no weight in the consideration. When the argument respects his attributes, they are of weight, but are then to be taken in conjunction with the unexceptional evidences which we possess of skill, power and benevolence displayed. Which evidences, in strength, number and variety, may so overpower apparent blemishes as to induce us upon the most reasonable ground to believe that these last ought to be referred to some cause, though we be ignorant of it, other than defect of [our] knowledge or of benelovence in the author.

There may be also parts of plants and animals, as there were supposed to be of the watch, of which the operation is unknown. These form different cases, for the operation may be unknown yet the use be certain. Thus it is with the lungs of animals. It does not, I think, appear that we are acquainted with the action of the air upon the blood, or in what manner that action is communicated by the lungs, yet we find that a very short suspension of their office destroys the life of the animal! In this case, therefore, we may be said to know the use though we be ignorant of its operation. Nearly the same thing may be observed of the lymphatic system. We suffer grievous inconveniences from its disorder, without being informed of the office which it sustains in the economy of our bodies. There may also be some few examples in which not only the operation is unknown, but in which experiments may seem to prove that the part is not necessary or even useful to the plant or animal in which it is found.

This is said to be the case with the spleen, which has been extracted from dogs without any sensible injury to their vital functions. [Such] instances may be numerous, [and] they will be so in proportion to our ignorance. Every improvement of knowledge diminishes their number. There is hardly, perhaps, a year passes that does not bring some operation to light which was before undiscovered. Instances where the part appears to be totally useless I believe to be extremely rare compared with the number of those of which the use is evident. But to this case, were it made out, may be applied the consideration which we suggested concerning the watch, that these superfluous parts do not negative the reasoning which we instituted concerning those parts which are useful and of which we know the use. The indication of contrivance with respect to them remains as it was before.

One atheistic way of replying to our observations upon the works of nature and to the proofs of a Deity which we perceive in them, is to tell us that all which we see must necessarily have had some form, and that it might as well be its present form as any other. Let us now apply this answer to the eye, as we did before to the watch. Something or other must have occupied that place in the animal's head. We will say also that it must have been of flesh, bone, membrane, [or] cartilage. But that it should have been an *eye*, knowing as we do what an eye comprehends: that it should have consisted first of a series of transparent lenses (very different in their substance from the rest of the body); of a black cloth or canvas (the only membrane of the body which is black!) spread out behind those lenses so as to receive the image, and placed at the precise geometrical distance at which, and at which alone, a distinct image could be formed; [and] thirdly of a large nerve between this membrane and the brain, without which the action of light upon the membrane, however modified, would be lost to the purposes of sensation. That this fortunate conformation of parts should have been the lot not of one individual out of many thousands, like the great prize in a lottery, but the happy chance of a whole species, nor of one species out of many thousands but of by far the greatest number of all that exist, under varieties suited to their exigencies, that all this should have taken place merely because *something* must have occupied those spaces in every animal's forehead, or that all this should be thought to be accounted for by the short answer that 'whatever was there must have had some form or other', is too absurd to be made more so by any augmentation!

We are not contented with this answer. We find no satisfaction in it by way of accounting for appearances of organization far short of those of the eye, such as we observe in fossil shells, petrified bones, or other substances which bear the vestiges of animal or vegetable recrements, but which, either in respect of utility or of the situation in which they are discovered, may seem accidental enough. It is no way of accounting for these things to say that the stone, for instance, must have contained some internal conformation or other. Nor does it mend the answer to add that it is no longer to be computed what the chances were against it. This is *always* to be computed when the question is whether a useful conformation be the produce of chance or not! I desire no greater certainty in reasoning than that by which chance is excluded from the present disposition of the natural world. Universal experience is against it. What does chance ever do for us? In the human body, for instance, chance may produce a wen, a wart, a mole, [or] a pimple – but *never* an eye! Amongst inanimate substances a clod, a pebble, [or] a liquid drop might be. But never was a watch, a telescope, [or] an organized body of any kind answering a valuable purpose by a complicated mechanism, the effect of chance. In no assignable instance hath such a thing existed without intention somewhere!

There is another answer which has the same effect as the resolving of things into chance, which answer would persuade us to believe that the eye, the animal to which it belongs, every other animal, every plant, indeed, every organized body which we see, are only so many out of the possible varieties and combinations of being which the lapse of infinite ages has brought into existence. That the present world is the relict of that variety, millions of other bodily forms having perished, being, by the defect of their constitution, incapable of preservation or continuance by generation. Now, there is no foundation whatever for this conjecture in anything which we observe in the works of nature. No such experiments are going on at present. No such energy operates as that which is here supposed and which should be constantly pushing into existence new varieties of beings. Nor are there any appearances to support an opinion that every possible combination of vegetable or animal structure has formerly been tried.

Moreover, the division of organized substances into animals and vegetables, and the distribution and sub-distribution of each into genera and species, which distribution is not an arbitrary act of the mind but founded in the order which prevails in nature, appear to me to contradict the supposition of the present world being the remains of an indefinite variety of existences, of a variety which rejects all plan. The hypothesis teaches that every possible variety of being hath, at one time or another, found its way into existence (by what cause or in what manner is not said!), and that those which were badly formed perished. But how or why those which survived should be cast into regular classes the hypothesis does not explain – or rather the hypothesis is inconsistent with this phenomenon!

The hypothesis, indeed, is hardly deserving of the consideration which we have given to it. What should we think of a man who, because we had never ourselves seen watches, telescopes, stocking-mills [or] steam engines made, knew not how they were made, or could prove by testimony when they were made or by whom, would have us believe that these machines, instead of deriving their structures from the thought and design of their inventors, in truth derive them from no other origin than this, that a mass of metals and other materials having run when melted into all possible figures, and combined themselves in all possible forms and shapes and proportions, these things which we see are what were left from the accident? I cannot distinguish the hypothesis as applied to the works of nature from this solution, which no one would accept as applied to a collection of machines!

To the marks of contrivance discovered in animal bodies, and to the argument deduced from them in proof of design and of a designing Creator, this turn is sometimes attempted to be given, namely that the parts were not intended for the use, but that the use arose out of the parts. This distinction is intelligible. A cabinet-maker rubs his mahogany with fish-skin. Yet it would be too much to assert that the skin of the dog-fish was made rough and granulated on purpose for the polishing of wood. Therefore the distinction is intelligible, but I think there is very little place for it in the works of nature. When roundly and generally affirmed, it amounts to such another stretch of assertion as it would be to say that all the implements of the cabinet-maker's workshop, as well as his fish-skin, were substances accidentally configurated, which he had picked up and converted to his use, that his adzes, saws, planes and gimlets were not made, as we suppose, to hew, cut, smooth, shape out or bore wood with, but that, these things being made, no matter with what design or whether with any, the cabinet-maker perceived that they were applicable to his purpose and turned them to account.

But again, so far as this solution is applied to those parts of animals, the action of which does not depend upon the will of the animal, it is fraught with still more absurdity. Is it possible to believe that the eye was formed without any regard to vision, that it was the animal itself which found out that, though formed with no such intention, it would serve to see with? And that the use of the eye as an organ of sight resulted from this discovery? The same question may be asked of the ear. The same for *all* the senses! None of the senses depend upon the election of the animal, neither upon his sagacity nor his experience. It is the impression that objects make upon them that constitutes their use. Under that impression he is passive.

Secondly, there are many parts of animal bodies which seem to depend upon the will of the animal in a greater degree than the senses do, yet with respect to which this solution is equally unsatisfactory. If we apply the solution to the human body, for instance, it forms itself into questions upon which no reasonable mind can doubt, such as whether the teeth were made expressly for the mastication of food, the feet for walking, the hands for holding. Or whether, these things being as they are in the animal's possession, his own ingenuity taught him that they were convertible to these purposes – though no such purposes were contemplated in their formation. They would otherwise be capacities without objects, powers without employment. The web-foot determines, you say, the duck to swim. But what would that avail if there were no water to swim in? The hooked bill and sharp talons of one species of bird determine it to prey upon animals. The straight bill and weak claws of another species determine it to pick up seeds. But neither determination could take effect in providing for the sustenance of the birds if animal bodies and seeds did not lie within their reach. The proboscis with which the bee is furnished determines him to seek for honey. But what would that signify if flowers supplied none? Faculties thrown down upon animals at random and without reference to the objects amidst which they are placed, would not produce to them the services and benefits which we see. And if there be that reference, then there is intention!

Lastly, the solution fails entirely when applied to plants. The parts of plants answer their uses without any concurrence from the will or choice of the plant.

Others have chosen to refer everything to a 'principle of order' in nature. A principle of order is the word, but what is meant by a principle of order as different from an intelligent Creator has not been explained, either by definition or example. And, without such explanation, it should seem to be a mere substitution of words for reasons, names for causes. Order itself is only the adaptation of means to an end. The principle of order therefore can only signify the mind and intention which so adapts them. Was a watch ever produced by a principle of order? And why not a watch as well as an eye?

A principle of order, acting blindly and without choice, is negatived by the observation that order is not universal. Which it would be if it issued from a constant and necessary principle. Nor indiscriminate, which it would be if it issued from an unintelligent principle. Where order is wanted, there we find it. Where order is not wanted, [or] where, if it prevailed, it would be useless, there we do not find it. In the structure of the eye (for we adhere to our example) the most exact order is maintained. In the forms of rocks and mountains, in the coasts of continents and islands, in the shape of bays and promontories, no order is perceived because it would have been superfluous. No useful purpose would have arisen from moulding rocks and mountains into regular solids, bounding the ocean by geometrical curves, or from the map of the world resembling a table of diagrams in Euclid's *Elements*, or Simpson's *Conic Sections*!

Lastly, the confidence which we place in our observations upon the works of nature, in the marks we discover of contrivance, choice and design, and in our reasoning upon the proofs afforded us, ought not to be shaken, as it is sometimes attempted to be done, by bringing forward to our view the general imperfection of our knowledge. True fortitude of understanding consists in not suffering what we know to be disturbed by what we do not know. If we perceive a useful end, and means adapted to that end, we perceive enough for our conclusion. If these things be clear, no matter what is obscure, the argument is finished. It concerns not the proof which these afford of design and of a designer, that there may perhaps be other parts, the agency or effect of which we can give no account. I take it to be a general way of infusing doubts into the mind to recall its own ignorance, to tell us that upon these subjects we know little, [and] that little imperfectly. These suggestions so fall in with our consciousness as sometimes to produce a general distrust of our faculties and conclusions. But this is an unfounded jealousy. The uncertainty of one thing does not necessarily affect the certainty of another. Before we yield in any particular instance to the scepticism this sort of insinuation would induce, we ought accurately to ascertain whether our ignorance or doubt concern those precise points upon which our conclusion rests. Other points are nothing! A just reasoner removes matters not strictly connected with his argument. Beyond these, his knowledge and his ignorance are alike relative!

Chapter Six

Were there no example in the world of contrivance except that of the eye, it would be alone sufficient to support the conclusion which we draw from it as to the necessity of an intelligent Creator. It could never be got rid of, because it could not be accounted for by any other supposition which did not contradict all the principles we possess of knowledge – the principles according to which things turn out to be true or false. And what I wish under the present chapter to observe is that if other parts of nature were inaccessible to our inquiries, or even if other parts of nature presented nothing to our examination but disorder and confusion, the validity of this example would remain the same. If there were but one watch in the world, it would not be less certain that it had a maker!

If we had never in our lives seen any but one single kind of hydraulic machine, we should be as perfectly assured that it proceeded from the hand and thought and skill of a workman as if we had visited a museum and saw there twenty different kinds of machine for drawing water, or a thousand different kinds for other purposes! Of this point, each machine is a proof independently of all the rest. So it is with the evidences of a Divine agency. The proof is not a conclusion which lies at the end of a chain of reasoning, of which chain each instance of contrivance is only a link, and of which if one link fail the whole falls. The eye proves it without the ear, the ear without the eye. The proof in each example is complete, for when the design of the part and the conduciveness of its structure to that design is shown, the mind may set itself at rest. No future consideration can detract anything from the force of the example.

Chapter Seven

I challenge any man to produce, in the joints and pivots of the most complicated or the most flexible machine that was ever contrived, a construction more artificial, or more *evidently* artificial, than that which is seen in the vertebrae of the human neck. Two things were to be done. The head was to have the power of bending forward and backward, as in the act of nodding, stooping, [or] looking upward and downward, and at the same time of turning itself round upon the body to a certain extent – [say] a hundred-and-twenty degrees of a circle.

For these two purposes, two distinct contrivances are employed. First, the head rests immediately upon the uppermost of the vertebrae, and is united to it by a hinge-joint. Upon which joint the head plays freely forward and backward, as far either way as is necessary or as the ligament allows – which was the first thing required. But then the rotatory motion is unprovided for. Therefore, secondly, to make the head capable of this, a further mechanism is introduced, not between the head and the upper bone of the neck which is where the hinge is, but between that bone and the next underneath it. It is a mechanism resembling a tenon and mortice.

This second, or uppermost bone but one, has what anatomists call a *process*, a projection somewhat similar in size and shape to a tooth. Which tooth, entering a corresponding hole or socket in the bone above it, forms a pivot or axle upon which that upper bone, together with the head which it supports, turns freely in a circle and as far in the circle as the attached muscles permit. Thus are both motions perfect without interfering with each other.

When we nod the head, we use the hinge-joint which lies between the head and the first bone of the neck. When we turn the head round, we use the tenon and mortice, which runs between the first bone of the neck and the second. We see the same contrivance and the same principle employed in the frame or mounting of a telescope. This is exactly the mechanism which is applied to the motion of the head. Will anyone here doubt the existence of counsel and design? – except it be by that debility of mind which can trust to its own reasonings in nothing!

We may add that it was on another account expedient that the motion of the head backward and forward should be performed upon the upper surface of the first vertebra, for if the first vertebra itself had bent forward, it would have brought the spinal marrow at the very beginning of its course upon the point of the tooth.

✳ ✳ ✳ ✳ ✳

Another mechanical contrivance not unlike the last in its object, but different and original in its means, is seen in the fore-arm, that [is] in the arm between the elbow and the wrist. Here, for the perfect use of the limb, two motions are wanted, a motion of the elbow backward and forward, which is called a reciprocal motion, and a rotatory motion by which the palm of the hand may be turned upward. How is this managed?

The fore-arm, it is well known, consists of two bones lying alongside each other, but touching only towards the ends. One, and only one of these bones is joined to the cubit or upper part of the arm at the elbow. The other to the hand at the wrist. The first, by means at the elbow of a hinge-joint (which allows only motion in the same plane), swings backward and forward, carrying along with it the other bone and the whole fore-arm. In the meantime, as often as there is occasion to turn the palm upward, that other bone, to which the hand is attached, rolls upon the first by the help of a groove or hollow near each end of one bone, to which is fitted a corresponding prominence in the other.

If both bones had been joined to the cubit or upper arm at the elbow, or both to the hand at the wrist, the thing could not have been done. The first was to be at liberty at one end, and the other at the other, by which means the two actions may be performed together. The great bone which carries the fore-arm may be swinging upon its hinge at the elbow, at the very time that the lesser bone which carries the hand may be turning round it in the grooves. The management also of these grooves, or rather of the tubercles and grooves, is very observable. The two bones are called the radius and the ulna. Towards the elbow, a tubercle of the radius plays into the socket of the ulna, whilst towards the wrist the radius finds the socket and the ulna the tubercle.

A single bone in the fore-arm, with a ball and socket joint at the elbow which admits of motion in all directions, might in some degree have answered the purpose of both moving the arm and turning the hand. But how much better it is accomplished by the present mechanism any person may convince himself who puts the ease and quickness with which he can shake his hand at the wrist circularly (moving likewise if he pleases his arm at the elbow at the same time), in competition with the comparatively slow and laborious motion with which his arm can be made to turn round at the shoulder by the aid of a ball and socket joint.

✳ ✳ ✳ ✳ ✳

The spine, or back-bone, is of very wonderful construction, [for] various difficult and almost inconsistent offices were to be executed. It was to be firm yet flexible (now I know no chain made by art which is both these, for by firmness I mean not only strength but stability!); firm, to support the erect position of the body, [and] flexible to allow the bending of the trunk in all degrees of curvature. It was also (which is another and quite distinct purpose from the rest) to become a pipe or conduit for the safe conveyance from the brain of the most important fluid of the animal frame upon which all voluntary motion depends – the spinal marrow, a substance not only of the first necessity to action, if not to life, but of a nature so delicate and tender, so susceptible and so impatient of injury, that any unusual pressure upon it, or any considerable obstruction of its course, is followed by paralysis or death!

Now the spine was not only to furnish the main trunk for the passage of the medullary substance from the brain, but to give out in the course of its progress small nerves [and to] distribute this exquisite supply to every part of the body. The same spine was also to serve another use not less wanted than the preceding, [namely] to afford a fulcrum, stay or basis (or, more properly speaking, a series of these) for the insertion of the muscles which are spread over the trunk of the body, in which trunk there are not, as in the limbs, cylindrical bones to which they can be fastened, and likewise to furnish a support for the ribs.

Bespeak of a workman a piece of mechanism which shall comprise all these purposes, and let him set about to contrive it. Let him try his skill upon it. Let him feel the difficulty of accomplishing the task before he be told how the same thing is effected in the animal frame. Nothing will enable him to judge so well of the wisdom which has been employed. Nothing will dispose him to think of it so truly. First, for the firmness, yet flexibility, of the spine. It is composed of a great number of bones (in the human subject, twenty-four), joined to one another and compacted by broad bases. The breadth of the bases upon which the parts severally rest, and the closeness of the junction, give to the chain its firmness and stability. The number of parts, and consequent frequency of joints, [give it] its flexibility. Which flexibility, we may also observe, varies in different parts of the chain. [It] is least in the back where strength more than flexure is wanted, greater in the loins which, it was necessary, should be more supple than the back, and greatest of all in the neck for the free motion of the head.

Then, secondly, in order to afford a passage for the descent of the medullary substance, each of these bones is bored through in the middle in such a manner that, when put together, the hole in one bone falls into a line and corresponds with the holes in the two bones contiguous to it. By which means the perforated pieces, when joined, form an entire, close, uninterrupted channel, at least while the spine is upright and at rest. But, as a settled posture is inconsistent with its use, a great difficulty still remained, which was to prevent the vertebrae shifting upon one another so as to break the line of the canal as the body moves or twists, or the joints gaping externally whenever the body is bent forward and the spine made to take the form of a bow. These dangers, which are mechanical, are mechanically provided against.

The vertebrae, by means of their processes and projections, and of the articulations which some of these form with one another at their extremities, are so locked in and confined as to maintain in what are called the bodies or broad surfaces of the bones the relative position nearly unaltered, and to throw the change and the pressure caused by flexion almost entirely upon the intervening cartilages, the springiness and unyielding nature of whose substance admits of all the motion which is necessary to be performed upon them without any chasm being produced by a separation of the parts! I say of all the motion which is necessary, for although we bend our backs to every degree almost of inclination, the motion of each vertebra is very small, such is the advantage we receive from the chain being composed of so many links, the spine of so many bones. Had it consisted of three or four bones only, in bending the body the spinal marrow must have been bruised at every angle.

The reader need not be told that these intervening cartilages are gristles, and he may see them in perfection in a loin of veal. Their form also favours the same intention. They are thicker before than behind, so that when we stoop forward the compressible substance of the cartilage, yielding in its thicker and anterior part to the force which squeezes it, brings the surfaces of the adjoining vertebrae nearer to being parallel with one another than they were before, instead of increasing the inclination of their planes, which must have occasioned a fissure or opening between them.

Thirdly, for the medullary canal giving out in its course, and in a convenient order, a supply of nerves to different parts of the body, notches are made in the upper and lower edge of every vertebra, two on each edge equidistant on each side from the middle line of the back. When the vertebrae are put together, these notches, exactly fitting, form small holes through which the nerves at each articulation issue out in pairs in order to send their branches to every part of the body with an equal bounty.

The fourth purpose assigned to the same instrument is the insertion of the bases of the muscles, and the support of the ends of the ribs. And for this fourth purpose, especially the former part of it, a figure, specifically suited to the design and unnecessary for other purposes, is given to the constituent bones. Whilst they are plain and round and smooth towards the front, where any roughness or projection might have wounded the adjacent viscera, they run out behind and on each side into long processes, to which processes the muscles necessary to the motions of the trunk are fixed, and fixed with such art that whilst the vertebrae supply a basis for the muscles, the muscles help to keep these bones in their position, or by their tendons to tie them together.

That most important property, strength, was to be still more specially consulted, for where so many joints were concerned, and where in every one derangement would have been fatal, it became a subject of studious precaution. For this purpose, the vertebrae are articulated by means of processes, and these so lock in with and overwrap one another as to secure the body of the vertebra not only from accidentally slipping, but even from being pushed out of its place by any violence short of that which would break the bone!

I have often remarked and admired this structure in the hare. In this, as in many instances, a plain observer of animal economy may spare himself the disgust of being present at human dissections, and yet learn enough for his information and satisfaction by examining the bones of the animals which come upon his table. Let him take, for example, into his hands a piece of the clean-picked bone of a hare's back, consisting, we will suppose, of three vertebrae. He will find the middle bone of the three so implicated by means of its projections or processes with the bone on each side of it, that no pressure which he can use will force it out of its place between them. It will give way neither forward nor backward, nor on either side. In whichever direction he pushes, he perceives in the form or overlapping of the bones an impediment opposed to his attempt – a check and guard against dislocation!

In one part of the spine he will find a still further fortifying expedient in the mode according to which the ribs are annexed to the spine. Each rib rests upon two vertebrae. That is the thing to be remarked, and anyone may remark it in carving a neck of mutton. The manner of it is this: The end of the rib is divided by a middle ridge into two surfaces. Which surfaces are joined to the bodies of two contiguous vertebrae, the ridge applying itself to the intervening cartilage. Now this is the very contrivance which is employed in the famous iron bridge at my door at Bishop Wearmouth – and for the same purpose of stability! The cheeks of the bars which pass between the arches, ride across the joints by which the pieces composing each arch are united. Each cross-bar rests upon two of these pieces at their place of junction, and by that position resists, at least in one direction, any tendency in either piece to slip out of its place. Thus perfectly, by one means or the other, is the danger of slipping laterally, or of being drawn aside out of line, provided against!

To withstand the bones being pulled asunder longitudinally, a strong membrane runs from one end of the chain to the other, sufficient to resist any force which is ever likely to act in the direction of the back. The general result is that not only the motions of the human body necessary for the ordinary offices of life are performed with safety, but that it is an accident hardly ever heard of that even the gesticulations of a harlequin distort his spine. Upon the whole, and as a guide to those who may be inclined to carry the consideration of this subject further, there are three views under which the spine ought to be regarded, and in all which it cannot fail to excite our admiration. These views relate to its articulations, its ligaments, and its perforation, and to the corresponding advantages which the body derives from it for action, for strength, and for that which is essential to every part, a secure communication with the brain.

The structure of the spine is not in general different in different animals. In the serpent, however, it is considerably varied, but with a strict reference to the conveniency of the animal. For whereas in quadrupeds the number of vertebrae is from thirty to forty, in the serpent it is nearly one hundred and fifty. [And] whereas in men and quadrupeds the surfaces of the bones are flat, and these flat surfaces laid one against the other and bound tight by sinews, in the serpent the bones play one within another like a ball and socket so that they have a free motion upon one another in every direction. That is to say, in men and quadrupeds firmness is more consulted, in serpents pliancy. Yet even pliancy is not obtained at the expense of safety. The back-bone of a serpent, for coherence and flexibility, is one of the most curious pieces of animal mechanism with which we are acquainted. The chain of a watch (I mean the chain which passes between the spring-barrel and the fusee) which aims at the same properties, is but a bungling piece of workmanship in comparison with that of which we speak!

The reciprocal enlargement and contraction of the chest to allow for the play of the lungs, depends upon a simple, yet beautiful, mechanical contrivance, referable to the structure of the bones which enclose it – the ribs articulated to the back-bone, or rather to its side projections obliquely. That is, in their natural position they bend or slope from the place of articulation downwards. But the basis upon which they rest at this end being fixed, the consequence of the obliquity or inclination downwards is that when they come to move,

70

whatever pulls the ribs upwards necessarily, [and] at the same time, draws them out, and that whilst the ribs are brought to a right angle with the spine behind, the sternum or [that] part of the chest to which they are attached in front, is thrust forward. The simple action of the muscles does the business, whereas if the ribs had been articulated with the vertebrae at right angles, the cavity of the thorax could never have been further enlarged by a change of their position. If each rib had been a rigid bone, articulated at both ends to fixed bases, the whole chest had been immoveable. Keill has observed that the breast-bone, in an easy inspiration, is thrust out one-tenth of an inch. And he calculates that this, added to what is gained to the space within the chest by the flattening or descent of the diaphragm, leaves room for forty-two cubic inches of air to enter at every drawing-in of the breath. When there is a necessity for a deeper and more laborious inspiration, the enlargement of the capacity of the chest may be so increased by effort that the lungs may be distended with seventy or a hundred such cubic inches. The thorax, says Schelhammer, forms a kind of bellows such as never have been, nor probably will be, made by an artificer!

The patella, or knee-pan, is a curious little bone, in its form and office unlike any other bone of the body. It is circular, the size of a crown piece, pretty thick, a little convex on both sides, and covered with a smooth cartilage. It lies upon the front of the knee, and the powerful tendons by which the leg is brought forward, pass through it (or rather it makes a part of their continuation) from their origin in the thigh to their insertion in the tibia. It protects both the tendon and the joint from any injury which either [of them] might suffer by the rubbing of one against the other, or by the pressure of unequal surfaces. It also gives to the tendons a very considerable mechanical advantage by altering the line of their direction and by advancing it further out from the centre of motion, and this upon the principles of the resolution of force, upon which principles all machinery is founded.

These are its uses. But what is most observable in it, is that it appears to be supplemental, as it were, to the frame. Added, as it should almost seem, afterward – not quite necessary, but very convenient! It is separate from the other bones. That is, it is not connected with any other bones by the common mode of union. It is soft, or hardly formed, in infancy, and produced by an ossification, the inception or progress of which no account can be given from the structure or exercise of the part.

The shoulder-blade is, in some material respects, a very singular bone, appearing to be made so expressly for its own purpose, and so independently. In such quadrupeds as have no collar-bones, which are by far the greater number, the shoulder-blade has no bony communication with the trunk, either by a joint or process or in any other way. It does not grow to, or out of, any other bone of the trunk. In strictness, it forms no part of the skeleton. It is bedded in the flesh, attached only to the muscles. It is no other than a foundation bone for the arm, laid in, separate, as it were, and distinct. The lower limbs connect themselves at the hip with bones which form part of the skeleton. But this connection in the upper limbs being wanting, a basis whereupon the arm might be articulated was to be supplied for the purpose.

✳ ✳ ✳ ✳ ✳

Of the Joints

The above are a few examples of bones made remarkable by their configuration. But to almost all the bones belong joints, and in these, still more clearly than in the form or shape of the bones themselves, are seen both contrivance and contriving wisdom. Every joint is a curiosity, and is also strictly mechanical. There is the hinge-joint and the mortice and tenon [or ball and socket] joint, each as manifestly and as accurately defined as any which can be produced out of a cabinet-maker's shop, and one or the other prevails as either is adapted to the motion which is wanted. A mortice and tenon, or ball and socket joint, is not required at the knee, the leg standing in need only of a motion backward and forward in the same plane, for which a hinge-joint is sufficient. A mortice and tenon, or ball and socket joint, is wanted at the hip, [so] that not only the progressive step may be provided for, but the interval between the limbs may be enlarged or contracted at pleasure.

Now, observe what would have been the inconvenience if the case had been inverted – if the ball and socket joint had been at the knee, and the hinge-joint at the hip! The thighs must have been kept constantly together, and the legs have been loose and straddling. There would have been no use that we know of in being able to turn the calves of the legs before, and there would have been great confinement by restraining the motion of the thighs to one plane. The disadvantage would not have been less if the joints at the hip and knee had been both of the same sort – both balls and sockets, or both hinges! Yet why, independently of utility and of a Creator who consulted that utility, should the same bone (the thigh bone) be rounded at one end and channelled at the other?

The hinge-joint is not formed by a bolt passing through the two parts of the hinge, thus keeping them in their places, but by a different expedient. A strong, tough, parchment-like membrane, rising from the receiving bones and inserted all round the receiving bones a little below their heads, encloses the joint on every side. This membrane ties, confines, and holds the ends of the bones together, keeping the corresponding parts of the joint in close application to each other.

For the ball and socket joint, there is in some important joints an additional security, a short, strong, yet flexible ligament inserted by one end into the head of the ball, [and] by the other into the bottom of the cup, which ligament keeps the two parts of the joint so firmly in their place that none of the motions which the limb naturally performs, none of the jerks and twists to which it is ordinarily liable, nothing less indeed that the utmost and the most unnatural violence, can pull them asunder. It is hardly imaginable how great a force is necessary even to stretch, still more to break, this ligament. Yet so flexible is it as to oppose no impediment to the suppleness of the joint. By its situation also, it is inaccessible to injury from sharp edges. As it cannot be ruptured (such is its strength), so it cannot be cut except by an accident which would sever the limb. If I had been permitted to frame a proof of contrivance such as might satisfy the most distrustful enquirer, I know not whether I could have chosen an example more unequivocal or more free from objection than this ligament. For the purpose of exciting admiration for the Creator's works, we diversify our views. We multiply examples. But for the purpose of strict argument, one clear instance is sufficient. And not only sufficient, but capable perhaps of generating a firmer assurance than what can arise from a divided attention.

The hinge-joint does not, it is manifest, admit of a ligament of the same kind with that of the ball and socket joint. The strong, firm, investing membrane above described accompanies it in every part, and, in particular joints, this membrane, which is properly a ligament, is considerably stronger on the sides than either before or behind in order that the convexities may play true in their concavities, and not be subject to slip sideways, which is the chief danger, for the muscular tendons generally restrain the parts from going further than they ought to go in the plane of their motion. In the knee, which is a joint of this form and of greater importance, there are superadded to the common provisions for the stability of the joint, two strong ligaments which cross each other, and cross each other in such a manner as to secure the joint from being displaced in any assignable direction. 'I think,' says Cheselden, 'that the knee cannot be completely dislocated without breaking the cross-ligaments.' We can hardly help comparing this with the binding up of a fracture, where the fillet is almost always strapped across for the sake of giving firmness and strength to the bandage.

Another no less important joint, is the ankle. Yet though important, small, and on that account more liable to injury. Now this joint is strengthened, i.e. is defended from dislocation, by two remarkable processes or prolongations of the bones of the leg, which processes form the protuberances that we call the inner and outer ankle. It is part of each bone going down lower than the other part, and thereby overlapping the joint, so that, if the joint be in danger of slipping outward, it is curbed by the inner projection, i.e. that of the tibia; [and] if inward, by the outer projection, i.e. that of the fibula. Between both, it is locked in its position. I know no account that can be given of this structure except its utility. Why should the tibia terminate at its lower extremity with a double end, and the fibula the same, but to barricade the joint on both sides by a continuation of the thickness of the bone over it?

The joint at the shoulder compared with the joint at the hip, though both ball and socket joints, discovers a difference in their forms and proportions well suited to the different offices which the limbs have to execute. The cup or socket at the shoulder is much shallower and flatter than it is at the hip, and is also in part formed of cartilage set round the rim of the cup. The socket, into which the head of the thigh-bone is inserted, is deeper, and made of more solid materials. This agrees with the duties assigned to each part. The arm is an instrument of motion, principally if not solely. Accordingly, the shallowness of the socket at the shoulder, and the yieldingness of the cartilaginous substance with which its edge is set round, and which in fact composes a considerable part of its concavity, are excellently adapted for the allowance of a free motion and a wide range, both which the arm wants. Whereas the lower limb, forming a part of the column of the body, [and] having to support the body as well as to be the means of its locomotion, firmness was to be consulted as well as action. With a capacity for motion in all directions indeed, as at the shoulder, but not in any direction to the same extent as the arm, was to be united stability or resistance to dislocation.

Hence the deeper excavation of the [hip's] socket and the presence of a lesser proportion of cartilage upon the edge. The suppleness and pliability of the joints we experience every moment, and the firmness of animal articulation, the property we have hitherto been considering, may be judged of this single observation, that, at any given moment in time, there are millions of animal joints in complete repair and use for one that is dislocated, and this notwithstanding the contortions and wrenches to which the limbs of animals are continually subject!

* * * * *

The joints, or rather the ends of the bones which form them, display also in their configuration another use. The nerves, blood-vessels and tendons, which are necessary to the life or motion of the limbs, must, it is evident, in their way from the trunk of the body to the place of their destination, travel over the moveable joints, and it is no less evident that in this part of their course they will have to encounter the danger of compression, attrition or laceration. To guard fibres so tender against consequences so injurious, their path is in those parts protected with peculiar care by a provision in the figure of the bones themselves.

The nerves which supply the fore-arm, especially the inferior cubital nerves, are at the elbow conducted by a kind of covered way between the condyls, or rather under the inner extuberances of the bone which composes the upper part of the arm. At the knee, the extremity of the thigh-bone is divided by a sinus or cliff into two heads or protuberances, and these heads on the back part stand out beyond the cylinder of the bone. Through the hollow which lies between the hind parts of these two heads, that is to say under the ham between the hamstrings, and within the concave recess of the bone formed by the extuberances on each side, pass the great vessels and nerves which go to the leg. Who led these vessels by a road so defended and secured?

In the joint at the shoulder, in the edge of the cup which

receives the head of the bone, is a notch which is covered at the top with a ligament. Through this hole, thus guarded, the blood-vessels steal to their destination in the arm instead of mounting over the edge of the concavity.

* * * * *

In all joints, the ends of the bones which work against each other are tipped with gristle. In the ball and socket joint, the cup is lined and the ball capped with it. The smooth surface, the elastic and unfriable nature of cartilage, render it of all substances the most proper for the place and purpose. I should therefore have pointed this out amongst the foremost of the provisions which have been made in the joints for the facilitating of their action had it not been alleged that cartilage is only nascent or imperfect bone, and that the bone in these places is kept soft and imperfect in consequence of a more complete and rigid ossification being prevented from taking place by the continual motion and rubbing of the surfaces. Which being so, what we represent as a designed advantage, is an unavoidable effect. I am far from being convinced that this is a true account of the fact, or that if it were so, it answers the argument. To me, the surmounting of the ends of the bones with gristle, looks more like a plating with a different metal than like the same metal kept in a different state by the action to which it is exposed!

In some joints, very particularly in the knees, there are loose cartilages or gristles between the bones and within the joint, so that the ends of the bones, instead of working upon one another, work upon the intermediate cartilages. Cheselden has observed that the contrivance of a loose ring is practised by mechanics where the friction of the joints of any of their machines is great, as between the parts of crook-hinges of large gates, or under the head of the male screw of large vices. The cartilages of which we speak, have very much the form of these rings. The comparison moreover shows the reason why we find them in the knees rather than in other joints. It is an expedience, we have seen, which a mechanic resorts to only when some strong and heavy work is to be done. So here the thigh-bone has to achieve its motion at the knee with the whole weight of the body pressing upon it, and often, as in rising from our seat, with the whole weight of the body to lift. It should seem also from Cheselden's account that the slipping and sliding of the loose cartilages, though it be probably of a small and obscure change, humoured the motion of the end of the thigh-bone under the particular configuration which was necessary to it – and which configuration requires what he calls a variable socket, that is a concavity, the lines of which assume a different curvature in different inclinations of the bones!

✳ ✳ ✳ ✳ ✳

We have now done with the configuration. But there is also in the joints, common to them all, another exquisite provision manifestly adapted to their use, concerning which there can, I think, be no dispute – namely the regular supply of a mucilage more emollient and slippery than oil itself, which is constantly softening and lubricating the parts that rub upon each other, thereby diminishing the effect of attrition in the highest possible degree! For the continual secretion of this important liniment, and for the feeding of the cavities of the joint, glands are fixed near each joint, the excretory ducts of which glands, dripping with their contents, hang loose like fringes within the cavity of the joints. A late improvement in what are called friction-wheels, which consist of a mechanism so ordered as to be regularly dropping oil into a box which encloses the axis, the nave, and certain balls upon which the nave revolves, may be said in some sort to represent the contrivance in the animal joint – with this superiority however on the part of the joint, that here the oil is not only dropped, but made!

In considering the joints there is nothing, perhaps, which ought to move our gratitude more than the reflection [of] how well they wear. A limb shall swing upon its hinge, or play in its socket, many hundred times in an hour for sixty years together, without diminution of its agility, which is a long time for anything to last so worked and exercised as the joints.

This durability I should attribute in part to the provision which is made for the preventing of wear and tear, first, by the polish of the cartilaginous surfaces; secondly, by the healing lubrication of the mucilage; and in part to that astonishing property of assimilation, by which in every portion of the body, let it consist of what it will, substance is restored and waste repaired!

Chapter Eight

Muscles, with their tendons, are the instruments by which animal motion is performed. It will be our business to point out instances in which the disposition of these muscles is as strictly mechanical as that of the wires and strings of a puppet.

We may observe an exact relation between the joint and the muscles which move it. Whatever motion the joint, by its mechanical construction, is capable of performing, that motion the annexed muscles are capable of producing. For example, if there be, as at the knee and elbow, a hinge-joint capable of motion only in the same plane, the leaders as they are called, i.e. the tendons, are placed in directions parallel to the bone so as to produce that motion and no other. Whereas at the shoulder and the hip, where the ball and socket joint allows a rotatory or sweeping motion, tendons are placed in such a position, and pull in such a direction, as to produce the motion of which the joint admits. For instance, the sartorius, or tailor's muscle, rising from the spine [and] running diagonally across the thigh, and taking hold of the inside of the main bone of the leg a little below the knee, enables us to throw one leg and thigh over the other, giving effect at the same time to the ball and socket joint at the hip, and the hinge-joint at the knee!

There is, as we have seen, a specific mechanism in the bones for the rotatory motions of the head and hands. There is also, in the oblique direction of the muscles belonging to them, a specific provision for putting this mechanism into action. And mark the consent of uses: the oblique muscles would have been inefficient without that particular articulation, [and] that particular articulation would have been lost without the oblique muscles!

The oblique muscles attached to the head are so disposed as to be capable of steadying the [head] as well as moving it. After death, the head drops and rolls in every direction. So that it is by the equilibre of the muscles [and] by the aid of a considerable and equipollent muscular force in constant exertion, that the head maintains its erect posture. The muscles here supply what would otherwise be a great defect in the articulation, for the joint in the neck, although admirably adapted to the motion of the head, is insufficient for its support. It is not only by the means of a most curious structure of the bones that a man turns his head, but by virtue of an adjusted muscular power that he even holds it up!

As another example of what we are illustrating – conformity of use between the bones and the muscles – it has been observed of the different vertebrae that their processes are exactly proportioned to the quantity of motion which the other bones allow of, and which the respective muscles are capable of producing.

A muscle acts only by contraction. Its force is exerted in no other way. When the exertion ceases, it relaxes itself. That is, it returns by relaxation to its former state, but without energy. This is the nature of muscular fibre, and being so it is evident that the reciprocal energetic motion of the limbs, by which we mean motion with force in opposite directions, can only be produced by opposite or antagonistic muscles – flexors and extensors answering to each other! For instance, the biceps and brachiaeus internus muscles placed in the front of the upper arm, by their contraction bend the elbow, and with such degree of force as the case requires or strength admits of. The relaxation of these muscles, after the effort, would merely let the fore-arm drop down. For the back stroke, therefore, [so] that the arm may not only bend at the elbow but also extend and straighten itself with force, other muscles, the longus and brevis brachiaeus externus and the anconaeus, placed on the hinder part of the arms, by their contractile twitch fetch back the fore-arm into a straight line with the cubit with no less force than that with which it was bent out of it.

The same thing obtains in all the limbs and in every moveable part of the body. A finger is not bent and straightened without the contraction of two muscles taking place. It is evident, therefore, that the animal functions require that particular disposition of the muscles which we describe by the name of antagonistic muscles. And they are accordingly so disposed. Every muscle is provided with an adversary. They act, like two sawyers, by an opposite pull, and nothing surely can more strongly indicate design and attention to an end than their being thus stationed.

The nature of muscular fibre being what it is, the purposes of the animal could be answered by no other. And not only the capacity for motion, but the aspect and symmetry of the body is preserved by the muscles being marshalled according to this order. The mouth is holden in the middle of the face, and its angle kept in a state of exact correspondency by two muscles drawing against and balancing each other. In a hemiplegia, when the muscle on one side is weakened, the muscle on the other side draws the mouth awry.

Another property of the muscles, which could only be the result of care, is their being almost universally so disposed as not to obstruct or interfere with one another's action. I know but one instance in which this impediment is perceived – we cannot easily swallow whilst we gape! The obstruction is in this instance attended with little inconvenience, but it shows what the effect is where it does exist, and what loss of faculty there would be if it were more frequent. Now, when we reflect upon the number of muscles, not fewer than four hundred and forty six in the human body known and named, how contiguous they lie to each other in layers, as it were, over one another, crossing one another, sometimes embedded in one another – an arrangement which leaves each to his liberty and full play – must necessarily require meditation and counsel.

The following is oftentimes the case with muscles. Their action is wanted where their situation would be inconvenient. In which case the body of the muscle is placed in some commodious position at a distance, and made to communicate with the point of action by slender strings. If the muscles which move the fingers had been placed in the palm or back of the hand, they would have swelled that part to an awkward and clumsy thickness. The beauty, the proportions of the part, would have been destroyed. They are therefore disposed in the arm, even up to the elbow, and act by long tendons strapped down at the wrist and passing under the ligaments to the fingers, and to the joints of the fingers which they are severally to move. In like manner, the muscles which move the toes and many of the joints of the foot, how gracefully are they disposed in the calf of the leg instead of forming and unwieldy tumefaction in the foot itself. The observation may be repeated of the muscle which draws the nictitating membrane over the eye. Its office is in the front of the eye, but its body is lodged in the back part of the globe, where it lies safe and where it encumbers nothing!

The great mechanical variety in the figure of the muscles may thus be stated. It appears to be a fixed law that the contraction of a muscle shall be towards its centre. Therefore the subject for mechanism on each occasion is so to modify the figure and adjust the position of the muscle as to produce the motion required agreeably with this law. This can only be done by giving to different muscles a diversity of configuration suited to their several offices and to their situation with respect to the work which they have to perform. On which account we find them under a multiplicity of forms and attitudes, sometimes with double, sometimes with treble tendons – sometimes with none! – sometimes one tendon to several muscles, [and] at other times one muscle to several tendons! The shape of the organ is susceptible of an incalculable variety, whilst the original property of the muscle, the law and line of its contraction, remains the same and is simple! Herein the muscular system may be said to bear a perfect resemblance to our works of art. An artist does not alter the native quality of his materials or their laws of action. He takes these as he finds them. His skill and ingenuity are employed in turning them, such as they are, to his account by giving the parts of his machine a form and relation in which these unalterable properties may operate to the production of the effects intended.

* * * * *

[It] can never too often be repeated how many things must go right for us to be an hour at ease! How many more for us to be vigorous and active! Yet vigour and activity are, in a vast plurality of instances, preserved in human bodies notwithstanding that the defect or disorder of a single pair out of the four hundred and forty six muscles which are employed, may be attended with grievous inconveniency. We may remark in how small a degree those who enjoy the perfect use of their organs know the comprehensiveness of the blessing, the variety of their obligation. They perceive a result, but they think little of the multitude of concurrences and rectitudes which go to form it.

The variety, quickness and precision of which muscular motion is capable, are seen, I think, in no part so remarkably as in the tongue. It is worth any man's while to watch the agility of his tongue, the wonderful promptitude with which it executes changes of position, and the perfect exactness. Each syllable of articulated sound requires for its utterance a specific action of the tongue and of the parts adjacent to it. The disposition and configuration of the mouth, appertaining to every letter and word, is not only peculiar but, if nicely and accurately attended to, perceptible to the sight, insomuch that curious persons have availed themselves of this circumstance to teach the deaf to speak and to understand what is said by others!

In the same person, and after his habit of speaking is formed, one and only one position of the parts will produce a given articulate sound correctly. How instantaneously are these positions assumed and dismissed! How numerous are the permutations, how various, yet how infallible! Arbitrary and antic variety is not the thing we admire, but variety obeying a rule conducing to an effect, and commensurate with exigencies

infinitely diversified. I believe also that the anatomy of the
tongue corresponds with these observations upon its activity.
The muscles of the tongue are so numerous, and so implicated
with one another, that they cannot be traced by the nicest
dissection. Nevertheless, (which is a great perfection of the
organ), neither the number nor the complexity, nor what might
seem to be the entanglement of its fibres, in any wise impede its
motion or render the determination or success of its efforts
uncertain!

* * * * *

I here entreat the reader's permission to step a little out of my
way to consider the parts of the mouth in some of their other
properties. It has been said, and that by an eminent physi-
ologist, that, whenever nature attempts to work two or more
purposes by one instrument, she does both or all imperfectly.
Is this true of the tongue, regarded as an instrument of speech
and taste? Or regarded as an instrument of speech, of taste,
and of deglutition? [It is] so much otherwise that many
persons, that is to say nine hundred and ninety nine out of a
thousand, by the instrumentality of this one organ, talk and
taste and swallow very well! In fact, the constant warmth and
moisture of the tongue, the thinness of the skin, the papillae
upon its surface, qualify this organ for its office of tasting as
much as its inextricable multiplicity of fibres do for the rapid
movements which are necessary to speech!

Animals which feed upon grass, have their tongues covered
with a perforated skin so as to admit the dissolved food to the
papillae underneath, which in the meantime remain defended
from the rough action of the unbruised spiculae.

There are brought together within the cavity of the mouth
more distinct uses, and parts executing more distinct offices,
than I think can be found lying so near to one another in any
other portion of the body, [namely] teeth of different shape,
first for cutting, secondly for grinding; muscles most artificially
disposed for carrying on the compound motion of the lower
jaw, half lateral and half vertical; saliva springing up in

different parts for the moistening of food; glands; a muscular constriction of a very peculiar kind in the back part of the cavity for the guiding of the prepared aliment into its passage towards the stomach, and in many cases for carrying it along that passage. For, although we may imagine this to be done by the weight of the food itself, it in truth is not so, even in the upright posture of the human neck – and most evidently is not the case with quadrupeds, with a horse for instance, in which, when pasturing, the food is thrust upward by muscular strength instead of descending of its own accord!

In the meantime, and within the same cavity, is going on another business altogether different from what is here described – that of respiration and speech. In addition, there-fore, to all that has been mentioned, we have a passage opened from this cavity to the lungs for the admission of air exclusively of every other substance. We have muscles, some in the larynx, and without number in the tongue, for the purpose of modulating that air in its passage, with a variety, a compass and precision of which no other musical instrument is capable!

And lastly, which in my opinion crowns the whole, we have a specific contrivance for dividing the pneumatic part from the mechanical, and for preventing one set of actions interfering with the other. Where various functions are united, the difficulty is to guard against the inconveniencies of a too great complexity. In no apparatus put together by art, do I know such multifarious uses so aptly combined as in the natural organisation of the human mouth, or where the structure, compared with the uses, is so simple. The mouth, with all these intentions to serve, is a single cavity, is one machine, with its parts neither crowded nor confused, and each unembarrassed by the rest – each at least at liberty in a degree sufficient for the end to be attained.

If we cannot eat and sing at the same moment, we can eat one moment and sing the next, the respiration proceeding freely all the while!

There is one case, however, of this double office, and that of the *earliest* necessity, which the mouth alone could not perform, and that is carrying on together the two actions of sucking [milk from a mother] and breathing. Another route, therefore, is opened for the air, namely through the nose, which lets the breath pass backward and forward whilst the lips, in the act of sucking, are necessarily shut close upon the body from which the nurtriment is drawn. This is a circumstance which always appeared to me worthy of notice. The nose would have been necessary although it had not been the organ of smelling. The making it the seat of a sense was superadding a new use to a part already wanted – [i.e.] was taking a wise advantage of an antecedent and a constitutional necessity.

* * * * *

But to return to that which is the proper subject of the present section, the celerity and precision of muscular motion. These qualities may be particularly observed in the execution of many species of instrumental music, in which the changes produced by the hand of the musician are exceedingly rapid, are exactly measured even when most minute, and display on the part of the muscles an obedience of action alike wonderful for its quickness and its correctness.

Or let a person only observe his own hand whilst he is writing, the number of muscles that are brought to bear upon the pen, how the joint and adjusted operation of several tendons is concerned in every stroke, yet that five hundred such strokes are drawn in a minute. Not a letter can be turned without more than one, or two, or three tendinous contractions, definite both as to the choice of the tendon and as to the space through which the contraction moves. Yet how currently does the work proceed! And when we look at it, how faithful have the muscles been to their duty – how true to the order which endeavour or habit hath inculcated! For let it be remembered that whilst a man's handwriting is the same, an exactitude of order is preserved whether he write well or ill. These two instances, of music and writing, show not only the quickness and precision of muscular action, but the docility!

We may also, upon the subject of muscles, observe that many of our most important actions are achieved by the combined help of *different* muscles. Frequently, a diagonal motion is produced by the contraction of tendons pulling in the direction of the sides of the parallelogram. This is the case, as hath been already noticed, with some of the oblique nutations of the head. Sometimes the number of co-operating muscles is very great. Dr Nieuentyt, in the *Leipsig Trans-actions*, reckons up a hundred muscles that are employed every time we breath. Yet we take in or let out our breath without reflecting what a work is thereby performed – what an apparatus is laid in of instruments for the service, and how many such contribute their assistance to the effect! Breathing with ease is a blessing of every moment. Yet of all others, it is that which we possess with the least consciousness. A man in an asthma is the only man who knows how to estimate it!

Mr Home has observed that the most important, and the most delicate actions, are performed in the body by the smallest muscles. And he mentions as his examples the muscles which have been discovered in the iris of the eye and the drum of the ear. The tenuity of these muscles is astonishing. They are microscopic hairs, must be magnified to be visible, yet are.they real, effective muscles. And not only such, but the grandest and most precious of our faculties, sight and hearing, depend upon their health and action.

The muscles act in the limbs with what is called a mechan-ical disadvantage. The muscle at the shoulder by which the arm is raised, is fixed nearly in the same manner as the load is fixed upon a steelyard – within a few decimals, we will say, of an inch from the centre upon which the steelyard turns. In this situation, we find that a very heavy draught is no more than sufficient to countervail the force of a small lead plummet placed upon the long arm of the steelyard at the distance of, perhaps, fifteen or twenty inches from the centre and on the other side of it. This is the disadvantage which is meant – and an absolute disadvantage no doubt it would be, if the object were to spare the force of muscular contraction. But observe how conducive is this constitution to animal conveniency.

Mechanism has always in view one or other of these two purposes: either to move a great weight slowly, and through a small space, or to move a light weight rapidly, through a considerable sweep. For the former of these purposes, a different species of lever and a different collocation of the muscles might be better than the present. But for the second, the present structure is the true one. Now so it happens that the second, and not the first, is that which the occasions of animal life principally call for! In what concerns the human body, it is of much more consequence to any man to be able to carry his hand to his head with due expedition, than it would be to have the power of raising from the ground a heavier load than he can lift at present. This last is a faculty which on some extraordinary occasions he may desire to possess. But the other is what he wants and uses every hour or minute. In like manner, a husbandman or gardener will do more execution by being able to carry his scythe, his rake or his flail with a sufficient dispatch through a sufficient space, than if, with greater strength, his motions were proportionably more confined and slow. It is the same with a mechanic in the use of his tools. It is the same also with other animals in the use of their limbs. In general, the vivacity of their motions would be ill exchanged for greater force under a clumsier structure.

* * * * *

We have offered our observations upon the structure of muscles in general. We have also noticed certain species of muscles. But there are also *single* muscles which bear marks of mechanical contrivance, appropriate as well as particular. Out of many instances of this kind, we select the following:

Of muscular actions, even of those which are well understood, some of the most curious are incapable of popular explanation, at least without the aid of plates and figures. This is in a great measure the case with a very familiar, but at the same time a very complicated motion – that of [dropping] the lower jaw, and with the muscular structure by which it is produced. One of the muscles concerned may, however, be described in such a manner as to be, I think, sufficiently comprehended for our present purpose.

The problem is to pull the lower jaw *down*. The obvious method should seem to be to place a straight muscle from the chin to the breast, the contraction of which would open the mouth and produce the motion required at once. But it is evident that the form and liberty of the neck forbid a muscle being laid in such a position, and that, consistently with the preservation of this form, the motion which we want must be effectuated by some muscular mechanism disposed further back in the jaw. The mechanism adopted is as follows:

A certain muscle called the diagastric, rises on the side of the face considerably *above* the insertion of the lower jaw, and comes down, being converted in its progress into a round tendon. Now it is manifest that the tendon, whilst it pursues a direction *descending* towards the jaw, must, by its contraction, pull the jaw up instead of down. What then was to be done? This, we find, is done – the descending tendon, when it is got low enough, is passed through a loop or ring, or pulley, in the os hyoïdes, and then made to ascend, and having thus changed its line of direction is inserted into the inner part of the chin! By which device, [namely] the turn of the loop, the action of the muscle (which in all muscles is contraction) that before would have pulled the jaw up, now necessarily draws it down! 'The mouth,' says Heister, 'is opened by means of this trochlea in a most wonderful and elegant manner.'

What contrivance can be more mechanical than the following, [namely] a slit in one tendon to let another tendon pass through it? This structure is found in the tendons which move the toes and fingers. The long tendon, as it is called, in the foot, which bends the first joint of the toe, passes *through* the short tendon which bends the second joint! Which course allows to the sinew more liberty, and a more commodious action, than it otherwise would have been capable of exerting. There is nothing, I believe, in a silk or cotton mill, in the belts or straps, or ropes by which motion is communicated from one part of the machine to another, that is more artificial, or more evidently so, than this perforation!

The next circumstance which I shall mention, under this head of muscular arrangement, is so decisive a mark of intention that it always appeared to me to supercede in some measure the necessity of seeking for any other observation upon the subject, and that circumstance is the tendons which pass from the leg to the foot, being bound down by a ligament at the ankle. The foot is placed at a considerable angle with the leg. It is manifest, therefore, that flexible strings, passing along the interior of the angle, if left to themselves would, when stretched, start [or jump] from it. The obvious preventive is to tie them down, and this is done in fact. Across the instep, or rather just above it, the anatomist finds a strong ligament *under* which the tendons pass to the foot. The effect of the ligament as a bandage can be made evident to the senses, for if it be cut the tendons start [or jump] up. The simplicity, yet the clearness of this contrivance, its exact resemblance to established resources of art, place it amongst the most indubitable manifestations of design with which we are acquainted.

There is also a further use to be made of the present example, and that is [that] it precisely contradicts the opinion that the parts of animals may have been all formed by what is called appetency, i.e. endeavour, perpetuated and imperceptibly working its effect through an incalculable series of generations. We have here no endeavour, but the reverse of it – a constant reluctance! The endeavour is all the other way. The pressure of the ligament constrains the tendons [and] the tendons react upon the pressure of the ligament! It is impossible that the ligament should ever have been generated by the exercise of the tendon, or in the course of that exercise, forasmuch as the force of the tendon perpendicularly resists the fibre which confines it, and is constantly endeavouring not to form, but to rupture and displace the threads of which the ligament is composed!

Keill has reckoned up in the human body four hundred and forty six muscles [which are] dissectible and describable, and hath assigned a use to every one of the number. This

cannot be all imagination. Bishop Wilkins hath observed from
Galen that there are at least ten several qualifications to be
attended to in each particular muscle, [namely] its proper
figure; its just magnitude; its fulcrum; its point of action,
supposing the figure to be fixed; its collocation, with respect
to its two ends, the upper and lower; the place; the position of
the whole muscle; [and] the introduction into it of nerves,
arteries [and] veins.

How are things including so many adjustments to be made,
or when made, how are they to be put together, without
intelligence?

Chapter Nine

The circulation of the blood through the bodies of men and quadrupeds, and the apparatus by which it is carried, compose a system and testify a contrivance [that is] perhaps the best understood of any part of the animal frame. The lymphatic system, or [else] the nervous system, may be more subtle and intricate. Nay, it is possible that in their structure they may be even more artificial than the sanguiferous. But we do not know so much about them.

The utility of the circulation of the blood I assume [to be] an acknowledged point. One grand purpose is plainly answered by it – the distributing to every part, every extremity, every nook and corner of the body the nourishment which is received into it by one aperture. What enters at the mouth, finds its way to the finger's ends. A more difficult mechanical problem could hardly, I think, be proposed than to discover a method of constantly repairing the waste, and of supplying an accession of substance to every part of a complicated machine at the same time.

The system presents itself under two views. First, the disposition of the blood-vessels, i.e. the laying of the pipes. And secondly, the construction of the engine at the centre, [namely] the heart, for driving the blood through them. The disposition of the blood-vessels, as far as regards the supply of the body, is like that of the water-pipes in a city, [namely] large and main trunks branching off by smaller pipes (and these again by still narrower tubes) in every direction, and towards every part in which the fluid they convey can be wanted.

So far, the water-pipes which serve a town may represent the vessels which carry the blood from the heart. But there is another thing necessary to the blood which is not wanted for the water, and that is the carrying it back again to its source! For this office, a reversed system of vessels is prepared, which, uniting at their extremities with the extremities of the first system, collects the divided and sub-divided streamlets, first by capillary ramifications into larger branches, [and] secondly by these branches into trunks. And thus returns the blood (almost exactly inverting the order in which it went out) to the fountain when its motion proceeded. All which is evident mechanism.

The body, therefore, contains two systems of blood-vessels – arteries and veins. Between the systems there are also two differences suited to the functions which the systems have to execute. The blood, in going out [and] passing always from wider into narrower tubes, and in coming back from narrower into wider, it is evident that the impulse and pressure upon the sides of the blood-vessel will be much greater in one case than the other. Accordingly, the arteries which carry out the blood are formed of much tougher and stronger coats than the veins which bring it back. That is one difference. The other is still more artificial, or, if I may so speak, indicates still more clearly the care and anxiety of the artificer. Forasmuch as in the arteries, by reason of the greater force with which the blood is urged along them, a wound or rupture would be more dangerous than in the veins, these vessels are defended from injury not only by their texture but by their situation, and by every advantage of situation which can be given to them.

They are buried in sinuses, or they creep along grooves made for them in the bones. For instance, the under-edge of the ribs is sloped and furrowed solely for the passage of these vessels. Sometimes they proceed in channels, protected by stout parapets on either side. Which last description is remarkable in the bones of the fingers, these being hollowed out on the underside like a scoop, and with such a concavity that the fingers may be cut across to the bone without hurting the artery which runs along it! At other times the arteries pass in canals wrought in the substance, and in the very *middle* of

96

the substance, of the bone. This takes place in the lower jaw, and is found where there would otherwise be danger of compression by sudden curvature. All this care is wonderful, yet not more than the importance of the case required. To those who venture their lives in a ship, it has been often said that there is only an inch-board between them and death. But in the body itself, especially in the arterial system, there is in many parts only a membrane, a skin [or] a thread. For which reason the system lies deep. Whereas the veins, in which the mischief that ensues from injuring the coats is much less, lie in general above the arteries, come nearer to the surface, [and] are more exposed.

It may be further observed concerning the two systems taken together, that though the arterial, with its trunk and branches and small twigs, may be imagined to issue or proceed, [or] in other words to *grow* from the heart like a plant from its root, yet the venal, the returning system, can never be formed in this manner. The arteries might go on lengthening and sub-dividing indefinitely. But an inverted system continually *uniting* its streams instead of dividing, thus carrying back what the other system carried out, could not be referred to the same process.

✳ ✳ ✳ ✳ ✳

The next thing to be considered is the engine which works this machinery – the heart. For our purpose, it is unnecessary to ascertain the principle upon which the heart acts. Whether it be irritation excited by the contact of the blood, by the influx of the nervous fluid, or whatever else be the cause of its motion, it is something which is capable of producing in a muscular fibre reciprocal contraction and relaxation. This is the power we have to work with, and the enquiry is how this power is applied in the instance before us.

There is provided in the central part of the body a hollow muscle invested with spiral fibres running in both directions, the layers intersecting one another – in some animals, however, appearing to be semi-circular rather than spiral. By the contraction of these fibres, the sides of the muscular cavities are necessarily squeezed together so as to force out from them any fluid which they may contain. By the relaxation of the same fibres, the cavities are dilated and prepared to admit fluid. Into these cavities are inserted the great trunks, both of the arteries which carry out the blood, and of the veins which bring it back. This is a general account of the apparatus, and the simplest idea of its action is that by each contraction blood is forced by a syringe into the arteries. This produces at each pulse a motion and change in the mass of blood to the amount of what the cavity contains, which, in a full-grown human heart, is about an ounce.

How quickly these changes succeed one another, and by this succession how sufficient they are to support a circulation throughout the system, may be understood by the following computation abridged from Keill's *Anatomy*, p. 117, ed. 3: 'Each ventricle will at least contain one ounce of blood. The heart contracts four thousand times in one hour. From which it follows that there pass through the heart every hour, four thousand ounces, or three hundred and fifty pounds of blood. Now the whole mass of blood is said to be about twenty-five pounds, so that a quantity of blood passes through the heart fourteen times in one hour, which is about once every four minutes.'

Consider what an affair this is when we come to very large animals. The aörta of a whale is larger in bore than the main pipe of the water-works at London Bridge! And the water roaring in its passage through that pipe is inferior in impetus and velocity to the blood gushing from the whale's heart! Hear Dr Hunter's account of the dissection of a whale: 'The aörta measured a foot diameter. Ten or fifteen gallons of blood are thrown out of the heart at a stroke, with immense velocity, through a tube of a foot diameter. The whole idea fills the mind with wonder.'

The account which we have here stated, is imperfect. The heart performs this office, but it is in conjunction with another of equal curiosity and importance. It was necessary that the blood should be brought into contact with the air. I do not know that the chemical reason upon which this necessity is founded, has been yet sufficiently explored. It seems to be that the atmosphere which we breathe is a mixture of two kinds of air, one pure and vital, [and] the other noxious. When we have drawn in our breath, the blood in the lungs imbibes from the air its pure ingredient, and at the same time gives out corrupt air every time we expire. At least, by comparing the air which is breathed from the lungs with the air which enters the lungs, it is found to have lost some of its pure part, and to have brought away with it its impure part. Whether these experiments satisfy the question as to the need which the blood stands in of continual access of air, is not for us to inquire into, nor material to our argument. It is sufficient to know that in most animals such a necessity exists, and that the air, by some means or other, must be introduced into a near communication with the blood.

The lungs of animals are constructed for this purpose. They consist of blood-vessels and air-vessels lying close to each other, and whenever there is a branch of the trachea or wind-pipe, there is a branch accompanying it of the vein and artery, and the air-vessel is always in the middle between the blood-vessels. The internal surface of these vessels upon which the application of the air to the blood depends, would, if collected and expanded, be in a man equal to a superficies of fifteen feet square!

Now, in order to give the blood in its course the benefit of this organisation (and this is the part of the subject with which we are chiefly concerned), the following operation takes place. As soon as the blood is received by the heart from the veins of the body, and *before* it is sent out again into its arteries, it is carried by the force of the contraction of the heart, and by means of a separate and supplementary artery, to the lungs, and made to enter the vessels of the lungs. From which, after it has undergone the action whatever it be of that viscus, it is brought back by a large vein once more to the heart in order, when thus concocted and prepared, to be thence distributed anew into the system. This assigns to the heart a double office. The pulmonary circulation is a system within a system, and one action of the heart is the origin of both!

For this complicated function four cavities become necessary, and four are accordingly provided – two, called ventricles, which send out the blood, one into the lungs in the first instance, [and] the other into the mass after it has returned from the lungs; [and] two others also, called auricles, which receive the blood from the veins, one as it comes immediately from the body, [and] the other as the same blood comes a second time after its circulation through the lungs. So that there are two receiving cavities, and two forcing cavities.

The translation of the blood in the heart itself is after this manner. The receiving cavities respectively communicate with the forcing cavities and, by their contraction, unload the received blood into them. The forcing cavities, when it is their turn to contract, compel the same blood into the arteries. The account here given will not convey to a reader ignorant of anatomy anything like an accurate notion of the form, action or use of the parts. Nor can any short and popular account do this. [But] how well doth it execute its office! An anatomist who understood the structure of the heart, would expect, I think, from the complexity of its mechanism and the delicacy of many of its parts, that it should always be liable to derangement, or that it would soon work itself out. Yet shall this wonderful machine go night and day for eighty years together at the rate of a hundred thousand strokes every twenty-four hours, having at every stroke a great resistance to overcome, and shall continue this action for this length of time without disorder and without weariness!

From the account which has been given of the heart, it is evident that it must require the interposition of valves – that the success, indeed, of its action must depend on these, for when any one of its cavities contracts, the necessary tendency of the force will be to drive the enclosed blood not only into the artery where it ought to go, but also back again into the vein from which it flowed. In like manner, when by the relaxation of the fibres the same cavity is dilated, the blood would not only run into it from the vein, which was the course intended, but back from the artery through which it ought to be moving forward!

The way of preventing a reflux of the fluid in both these cases is to fix valves which, like flood-gates, may open a way to the stream in one direction, and shut up the passage against it in another. The heart, constituted as it is, can no more work without valves than a pump can. When the piston descends in a pump, if it were not for the stoppage by the valve beneath, the motion would only thrust down the water which it had before drawn up! A similar consequence would frustrate the action of the heart. Valves, therefore, are essential to the contrivance – and valves so disposed are accordingly provided!

There is some variety in the construction of these valves. Though all the valves of the body act nearly upon the same principle and are destined to the same use, in general, they consist of a thin membrane lying close to the side of the vessel, consequently allowing an open passage whilst the stream runs one way, but thrust out from the side by the fluid getting behind it, and opposing the passage of the blood when it would flow the other way. Where more than one membrane is employed, the different membranes only compose one valve. For instance, over the entrance of the right auricle of the heart, three of these membranes are fixed [and are] of a triangular figure, the bases of the triangles [being] fastened to the flesh, [with] the sides and the summits loose – but, though loose, connected by threads of a determinate length with small fleshy prominences adjoining. The effect of this construction is that, when the ventricle contracts, the blood, endeavouring to escape in all directions, gets between these membranes and the side of the passage and thereby forces them up into such a position that together they constitute a hollow cone, which cone, entirely occupying the passage, prevents the return of the blood into the auricle! Can anyone doubt of contrivance here, or is it possible to shut our eyes against the proof of it?

We may here repeat what we before observed concerning the ligaments of the body, that they could not be formed by any action of the parts themselves. Valves could not be so formed. Action and pressure are all against them. The blood, in its proper course, has no tendency to produce such things, and in its improper current has a tendency to prevent their production. Whilst we see, therefore, the use and necessity of this machinery, we can look to no other account of its origin and formation than the intending mind of a Creator. Here also, we cannot consider but with gratitude how happy it is that our vital motions are involuntary. We should have enough to do if we had to keep our hearts beating! We must have been continually upon the watch and continually in fear!

It might [also] perhaps be expected that an organ so precious [and] of such primary importance as the heart, should be defended by a case. The fact is, that a membranous purse made of strong, tough materials *is* provided for it – holding the heart within its cavity, sitting loosely and easily about it, guarding its substance without confining its motion, and containing a spoonful or two of water just sufficient to keep the surface in a state of suppleness and moisture! How should such a loose covering be generated by the action of the heart? Does not the enclosing of it show the care that has been taken of its preservation?

Chapter Ten

Amongst the vessels of the human body, another exquisite structure is the larynx. We all know that there go down the throat two pipes, one leading to the stomach, the other to the lungs. We know also that both these passages open into the bottom of the mouth, the gullet necessarily for the conveyance of food, and the wind-pipe. The difficulty was, the passages being so contiguous, to prevent the food, especially liquids, from entering the wind-pipe – the consequences of which error, when it does happen, is perceived by the compulsive throes that are instantly produced. This business, which is very nice, is managed in this manner:

The gullet opens into the mouth like the cone of a funnel. Into the side of this funnel, at the part which lies the lowest, enters the wind-pipe by a chink or slit, with a lid or flap, like a little tongue, accurately fitted to the orifice. The solids or liquids which we swallow pass over this lid or flap as they descend by the funnel into the gullet. Both the weight of the food and the action of the muscles concerned in swallowing, contribute to keep the lid close down upon the aperture whilst anything is passing – whereas by means of its natural cartilaginous spring, it raises itself a little as soon as the food is passed, thereby allowing a free inlet and outlet for the respiration of the lungs.

Such is its structure, and we may here remark the almost complete success of the expedient – how seldom it fails of its purpose compared with the number of instances in which it fulfils it! Reflect how frequently we swallow [and] how constantly we breathe. In a city-feast, for example, what deglutition – what anhelation! Yet does this little cartilage, the epiglottis, so securely guard the entrance of the wind-pipe, that whilst morsel after morsel, draught after draught, are coursing one another over it, an accident of a crumb or a drop slipping into this passage (which nevertheless must be opened for breath every second of time) excites in the whole company not only alarm by its danger, but surprise by its novelty. No two guests are choked in a century!

There is no room for pretending that the action of the parts may have gradually formed the epiglottis – I do not mean in the same individual, but in a succession of generations. Not only the action of the parts has no such tendency, but the animal could not live either without it or with it in a half-formed state! The species was not to wait for the gradual formation or expansion of a part which was, from the first, necessary to the life of the individual!

Not only is the larynx curious, but the whole wind-pipe possesses a structure adapted to its peculiar office. It is made up (as anyone may perceive by putting his fingers to his throat) of stout cartilaginous ringlets, placed at small and equal distances from one another. Now this is not the case with any other of the numerous conduits of the body. The use of these cartilages is to keep the passage for the air constantly open, which they do mechanically. A pipe with soft membranous coats, liable to collapse when empty, would not have answered here, although this be the general vascular structure which serves very well for those tubes which are kept in a state of perpetual distension by the fluid they enclose. Nevertheless (which is another particularity well worthy of notice), these rings are not complete, that is [they] are not cartilaginous and stiff all round. But their hinder part, which is contiguous to the gullet, is membranous and soft, easily yielding to the distensions of that organ occasioned by the descent of food. The same rings are also bevelled off at the upper and lower edges, the better to close upon one another when the trachea is compressed or shortened.

The constitution of the trachea may suggest likewise another reflection. The membrane which lines it inside is, perhaps, the most sensible, irritable membrane of the body. It rejects the touch of a crumb of bread or a drop of water with a spasm which convulses the whole frame. Yet, left to itself and its proper office – the intromission of air alone – nothing can be so quiet! It does not even make itself felt. A man does not know that he has a trachea! This capacity of perceiving with such acuteness this impatience of office, yet perfect ease when let alone, are properties one would have thought not likely to reside in the same subject. It is to the junction, however, of these almost inconsistent qualities in this as well as in some other delicate parts of the body, that we owe our safety and our comfort – our safety to their sensibility, [and] our comfort to their repose!

The larynx, or rather the whole wind-pipe taken together (for the larynx is only the upper part of the wind-pipe), besides its other uses, is also a musical instrument. That is to say, it is a mechanism expressly adapted to the modulation of sound, for it has been found upon trial that by relaxing or tightening the tendinous bands at the extremity of the wind-pipe, and blowing in at the other end, all the cries and notes might be produced of which the living animal was capable. It can be sounded, just as a pipe or flute is sounded!

Birds, says Bonnet, have at the lower end of the wind-pipe, a conformation like the reed of an *hautbois* for the modulation of their notes. A tuneful bird is a ventriloquist. The seat of the song is in the breast. The use of the lungs in the system has been said to be obscure. One use, however, is plain, and that is the formation, in conjunction with the larynx, of voice and speech. They are to animal utterance what the bellows are to an organ!

* * * * *

For the sake of method, we have considered animal bodies under three divisions, their bones, their muscles and their vessels. And we have stated our observations upon these parts separately. But this is to diminish the strength of the argument. The wisdom of the Creator is seen, not in their separate, but in their collective action, in their mutual subserviency and dependence, in their contributing together to one effect and one use. It has been said that a man cannot lift his hand to his head without finding enough to convince him of the existence of God. And it is well said, for he has only to reflect, familiar as this action is and simple as it seems to be, how many things are requisite for the performing of it.

Hitherto we seem to understand the mechanism pretty well, and understanding this we possess enough for our conclusion. Nevertheless, we have hitherto only a machine standing still, a dead organisation – an apparatus! To put the system in a state of activity, to set it at work, a further provision is necessary, [namely] a communication with the brain by means of nerves. We know the existence of this communication, because we can see the communicating threads and can trace them to the brain. Its necessity we also know, because if the thread be cut, the muscle becomes paralytic. But beyond this, we know little, the organisation being too minute and subtle for our inspection.

To what has been enumerated as officiating in the single act of a man's raising his hand to his head, must be added likewise all that is necessary and all that contributes to the growth, nourishment and sustentation of the limb, the repair of its waste, the preservation of its health such as the circulation of the blood through every part of it, its lymphatics, exhalants, absorbents, its excretions and integuments. All these share in the result, join in the effect, and how all these or any of them come together without a designing, disposing intelligence, it is impossible to conceive.

Chapter Eleven

Contemplating an animal in its collective capacity, we cannot forget to notice what a number of instruments are brought together, and often within how small a compass. It is a cluster of contrivances! In a canary bird, for instance, and in the single ounce of matter which composes his body (but which seems to be all employed), we have instruments for eating, for digesting, for nourishment, for breathing, for generation, for running, for flying, for seeing, for hearing, for smelling – each appropriate, [and] each entirely different from the rest. The human, or indeed the animal frame, considered as an assemblage, exhibits properties which have long struck my mind as indubitable evidences not only of design, but of a great deal of attention and accuracy in prosecuting the design.

[One such property] is the exact correspondency of the two sides of the same animal, the right hand answering to the left, leg to leg, eye to eye, one side of the countenance to the other, and with a precision to imitate which, forms one of the difficulties of statuary, and requires on the part of the artist a constant attention to this property of his work distinct from every other. It is the most difficult thing that can be to get a wig made even. Yet how seldom is the face awry? And what care is taken that it should not be so, the anatomy of its bones demonstrates. The upper part of the face is composed of thirteen bones, six on each side answering each to each, and the thirteenth, without a fellow, in the middle! The lower part of the face is in like manner composed of six bones, three on each side corresponding, and the lower jaw in the centre. In building an arch, could more be done in order to make the curve true, the parts equidistant in the middle, alike in figure and position?

[Another] property of animal forms is beauty. I do not mean relative beauty, or that of one individual above another. But I mean, generally, the provision which is made in the body of almost every animal to adapt its appearance to the perception of the animals with which it converses. In our own species, for example, only consider what the parts and materials are of which the fairest body is composed, and no further observation will be necessary to show how well these things are wrapped so as to form a mass which shall be capable of symmetry in its proportion and of beauty in its aspect. All which seems to be a strong indication of design studiously directed to this purpose.

It being once allowed that such a purpose existed with respect to *any* of the productions of nature, [then] we may refer with a considerable degree of probability other particulars to the same intention – the taints of flowers, the plumage of birds, the furs of beasts, the bright scales of fishes, the painted wings of butterflies and beetles, the rich colours and spotted lustre of many insects. In plants, especially in the flowers of plants, the principle of beauty holds a still more considerable place in their composition. Why, for one instance out of a thousand, does the corolla of the tulip, when advanced to maturity, change its colour? The purposes, so far as we can see, of vegetable nutrition might have been carried on as well by its continuing green! Why break into such a variety of colours? It seems a lame account to call it, as it has been called, a disease of the plant. Is it not more probable that this property, which is independent it would seem of the wants and utilites of the plant, was calculated for beauty [and] intended for display?

We possess a sense of beauty, however we come by it. It in fact exists. Things are not indifferent to this sense. All objects do not suit it. Many which we see are agreeable to it. Many others disagreeable. It is certainly not the effect of habit, because the most agreeable objects are often the most rare, [while] many which are very common continue to be offensive.

If this sense be acquired, it is the produce of the mind upon its sensations.

* * * * *

Of animal bodies, there is another property more curious than it is generally thought to be, which is the faculty of – standing! And it is more remarkable in two-legged animals than in quadrupeds, and, most of all, as being the tallest and resting upon the smallest base, in man. There is more, I think, of the matter than we are aware of. The statue of a man placed loosely upon its pedestal, would not be secure of standing half an hour. You are obliged to fix its feet to the block by bolts and solder, or the first shake, the first gust of wind, is sure to throw it down. Yet this statue shall express all the mechanical proportions of a living model. It is not, therefore, the mere figure, or merely placing the centre of gravity in the base, that is sufficient. Either the law of gravitation is suspended in favour of living substances, or something more is done for them in order to enable them to uphold their posture.

There is no reason whatever to doubt but that their parts descend by gravitation in the same manner as those of dead matter. The gift, therefore, appears to me to consist in a faculty of perpetually shifting the centre of gravity by a set of obscure, indeed, but of quick-balancing actions so as to keep the line of direction, which is a line drawn from that centre to the ground, within its prescribed limits. Of these actions it may be observed, first, that they constitute strength. The dead body drops down. The mere adjustment, therefore, of weight and pressure, which may be the same the moment after death as the moment before, does not support the column. In cases also of extreme weakness, the patient cannot stand upright.

Secondly, that these actions are only in a small degree voluntary. A man is seldom conscious of his voluntary powers in keeping himself upon his legs. A child learning to walk, is the greatest posture-master in the world. But art, if it may be so called, sinks into habit, and he is soon able to poise himself in a great variety of attitudes without being sensible either of caution or effort. But still there must be an aptitude of parts upon which habit can thus attach – a previous capacity of motions which the animal is thus taught to exercise. And the facility with which this exercise is acquired forms one object of our admiration.

What parts are principally employed, or in what manner each contributes its office, is, as hath already been confessed, difficult to explain. Perhaps the obscure motion of the bones of the feet may have their share in this effect. They are put in action by every slip or vacillation of the body, and seem to assist in restoring its balance. Certain it is, that this circumstance in the structure of the foot, [namely] its being composed of many small bones applied to and articulating with one another by diversely shaped surfaces instead of being made of one piece like the last of a shoe, is very remarkable. I suppose also that it would be difficult to stand firmly upon wooden legs, though their base exactly imitated the figure and dimensions of the sole of the foot. The alternation of the joints, the knee-joint bending backward, the hip-joint forward, the flexibility in every direction of the spine, especially in the loins and neck, appear to be of great moment in preserving the equilibrium of the body.

With respect to this last circumstance, it is observable that the vertebrae are so confined by ligaments as to allow no more slipping upon their bases than what is just sufficient to break the shock when any violent motion may occasion to the body. A certain degree also of tension of the sinews appears to be essential to an erect posture, for it is by the loss of this that the dead or paralytic body drops down. The whole is a wonderful result of combined powers and of very complicated operations. Indeed, that standing is not so simple a business as we imagine it to be, is evident from the strange gesticulations of a drunken man, who has lost the government of the centre of gravity.

We have said that this property is the most worthy of observation in the human body. But a bird, resting upon its perch or hopping upon a spray, affords no mean specimen of the same faculty. A chicken runs off as soon as it is hatched

110

from the egg. Yet a chicken, considered geometrically and with relation to its centre of gravity, its line of direction and its equilibrium, is a *very* irregular solid! Is this [a] gift, therefore, or instruction? May it not be said to be with great attention that nature hath balanced the body upon its pivots?

I observe also in the same bird a piece of useful mechanism of this kind – that the claws close of their own accord. Now let it be remembered, that this is the position of the limbs in which the bird rests upon its perch. And in this position it sleeps in safety, for the claws do their office in keeping hold of the support not by any exertion of voluntary power, which sleep might suspend, but by the traction of the tendons in consequence of the attitude which the legs and thighs take by the bird sitting down, and to which the mere weight of the body gives the force that is necessary.

* * * * *

Regarding the human body [and] the general conformations which obtain in it, we shall be led to observe what I call 'interrupted analogies'. The following are examples of what I mean by these terms, and I do not know how such critical deviations can, by any possible hypothesis, be accounted for without design.

All the bones of the body are covered with a periosteum except the teeth, where it ceases and an enamel of ivory, which saws and files will hardly touch, comes into its place. No one can doubt of the use and propriety of this difference, of the analogy being thus interrupted, of the rule which belongs to the conformation of the bones stopping where it does stop. For, had so exquisitely sensible a membrane as the periosteum invested the teeth, as it invests every other bone of the body, their action, necessary exposure and irritation, would have subjected the animal to continual pain. General as it is, it was not the sort of integument which suited the teeth. What they stood in need of was a strong, hard, insensible, defensive coat, and exactly such a covering is given to them in the ivory enamel which adheres to their surface.

The skin which clothes the rest of the body, gives way at the extremities of the toes and fingers to nails. A man has only to look at his hand to observe with what nicety and precision that covering which extends over every other part, is here super-ceded by a different substance and a different texture. Now, if either the rule had been necessary or the deviation from it accidental, this effect would not be seen. When I speak of the rule being necessary, I mean the formation of the skin being produced without design, and acting, as all ignorant causes must act, by a general operation. Were this the case, no account could be given of the operation being suspended at the finger's ends. [And] if the deviation were accidental, an error, an anomalism, were it anything else than settled intention, we should meet with nails upon other parts of the body [where] they would be scattered over the surface like pimples or warts.

All the great cavities of the body are enclosed by membranes except the skull. Why should not the brain be content with the same covering as that which serves for the other principal organs of the body? The heart, the lungs, the liver, the stomach, the bowels, have all soft integuments and nothing else. The muscular coats are all soft and membranous. I can see a reason for this distinction in the final cause, but in no other. The importance of the brain to life (which experience proves to be immediate), and the extreme tenderness of its substance, make a solid case more necessary for it than for any other part. And such a case the hardness of the skull supplies. When the smallest portion of this natural casket is lost, how carefully, yet how imperfectly, is it replaced by a plate of metal? If an anatomist should say that this bony protection is not confined to the brain, but is extended along the course of the spine, I answer that he adds strength to the argument. If he remark that the chest also is fortified by bones, I reply that I should have alleged this instance myself. [But] what distinguishes the skull from every other cavity is that the bony covering completely surrounds its contents, and is calculated not for motion, but solely for defence. Those hollows, likewise, and inequalities which we observe in the inside of the skull, and which exactly fit the folds of the brain, answer the important design of keeping the substance of the brain steady, and of guarding it against concussion.

Chapter Twelve

Whenever we find a general plan pursued, yet with such variations as are required by the subject to which it is applied, we possess in such plan and adaptation the strongest evidence that can be afforded of intelligence and design – an evidence which most completely excludes every other hypothesis! If the general plan proceeded from any fixed necessity in the nature of things, how could it accomodate itself to the various wants and uses under different circumstances and on different occasions? Arkwright's Mill was invented for the spinning of cotton. [But] we see it [also] employed for the spinning of wool, flax and hemp, with such modifications of the original plan as the texture of those different materials rendered necessary. Of the machine's being put together with design whilst we saw it only under one mode and in one form, when we came to observe it in its different applications, with such changes of structure as the special use in each case demanded, we could not refuse any longer our assent to the proposition that intelligence (including foresight, consideration [and] reference to utility) had been employed as well in the primitive plan as in the several changes and accomodations which it is made to undergo.

Very much of this reasoning is applicable to what has been called Comparative Anatomy. In their general economy, in the outlines of the plan, in the construction as well as offices of their principal parts, there exists between all large terrestrial animals a close resemblance. In all, life is sustained and the body nourished by nearly the same apparatus. The heart, the lungs, the stomach, the liver, the kidneys, are much alike in all. The same fluid circulates through their vessels, and nearly in the same order. The same cause, therefore, whatever that cause was, has been concerned in the origin [and] has governed the production of these different animal forms.

When we pass on to smaller animals, or to the inhabitants of a different element, the resemblance becomes more distant and obscure. But still the plan accompanies us. And, what we can never enough commend, and which it is our business at present to exemplify, the plan is attended through all its varieties and deflections by subserviences to special occasions and utilities.

The covering of different animals is the first thing which presents itself to our observation, and is in truth as much to be admired as any part of their structure. We have bristles, hair, wool, furs, feathers, quills, prickles, scales. Yet in this diversity of material and form, we cannot change one animal's coat for another without evidently changing it for the worse! – taking care, however, to remark that these coverings are, in many cases, armour as well as clothing, intended for protection as well as warmth.

The human animal is the only one which is naked, and the only one which can clothe itself. This is one of the properties which renders him an animal of all climates and seasons. He can adapt the warmth or lightness of his covering to the temperature his habitation. Had he been born with a fleece upon his back, although he might have been comforted by its warmth in high latitudes, it would have oppressed him by its weight and heat as the species spread towards the equator.

What art, however, has done for men, nature has in many instances done for those animals which are incapable of art. Their clothing, *of its own accord*, changes with their necessities. This is particularly the case with large quadrupeds which are covered with furs. Every dealer in hare-skins and rabbit-skins knows how much the fur is thickened by the approach of winter. It seems to be a part of the same constitution and the same design that wool, in hot countries, degenerates – as it is called – but in truth (most happily for the animals's ease)

116

passes into hair, whilst on the contrary that hair, in dogs of the polar regions, is turned into wool or something very like it. To which may be referred what naturalists have remarked, that bears, wolves, foxes, hares, which do not take [to] water, have the fur much thicker on the back than [on] the belly. Whereas in the beaver it is thickest upon the belly, as are the feathers in water-fowl.

The covering of birds, its lightness, its smoothness, its warmth, the disposition of the feathers all inclined backwards, the down about their stem, the overlapping of their tips, their different configuration in different parts, not to mention the variety of their colours, constitute a vestment for the body so beautiful and so appropriate to the life which the animal is to lead, as that, I think, we should have had no conception of anything equally perfect if we had never seen it. Let us suppose (what is possible only in supposition) a person who had never seen a bird, to be presented with a plucked pheasant, and bid to set his wits to work how to contrive for it a covering which shall unite the qualities of warmth, levity, and least resistance to the air – and the highest degree of each – giving it also as much of beauty and ornament as he could afford. *He* is the person to behold the work of the Deity!

The commendation will be increased by further examination. It is one of those cases in which the philosopher has more to admire than the common observer. Every feather is a mechanical wonder. If we look at the quill, we find properties not easily brought together – strength and lightness. I know few things more remarkable than the strength and lightness of the very pen with which I am writing. If we cast our eye to the upper part of the stem, we see a material made for the purpose, used in no other class of animals, and in no other part of birds – tough, light, pliant, [and] elastic. The pith also, which feeds the feathers, is neither bone, flesh, membrane nor tendon.

The artificial part of a feather is the beard, or as it is sometimes called, the vane. By the beards are meant the breadth of the feather, what we usually strip off from one side or both when we make a pen. The separate pieces, or laminae, of which the beard is composed are called threads, sometimes

filaments. Now the first thing which an attentive observer will
remark is, how much stronger the beard of the feather shows
itself to be when pressed in a direction perpendicular to its
plane, than when rubbed up or down in the line of the stem.
And he will soon discover the structure which occasions this
difference, [namely] the laminae whereof these beards are
composed, are flat and placed with their flat sides towards
each other, by which means, whilst they easily bend for the
approaching of each other, as anyone may perceive by drawing
his finger ever so lightly upwards, they are much harder to
bend out of their plane which is the direction in which they
have to encounter the impulse and pressure of the air, and in
which their strength is wanted and put to trial.

This is one particularity in the structure of a feather. A
second is still more extraordinary. Whoever examines a feather
cannot help taking notice that the threads, or laminae of which
we have been speaking, in their natural state *unite*! Their union
is something more than the mere apposition of loose surfaces.
They are not parted asunder without some degree of force.
Nevertheless, there is no glutinous adhesion between them.
Therefore, by some mechanical means or other, they catch or
clasp among themselves, thereby giving the beard, or vane, its
closeness of texture. Nor is this all. When two laminae, which
have been separated by accident or force, are brought together
again, they immediately reclasp! The connexion, whatever it
was, is perfectly recovered, and the beard of the feather
becomes as smooth and firm as if nothing had happened to
it. Draw your finger down the feather, which is against the
grain, and you break, probably, the junction of some of
the contiguous threads. Draw your finger up the feather, and
you restore all things to their former state. This is no common
contrivance!

And now for the mechanism by which it is effected. The
threads or laminae are interlaced with one another, and the
interlacing is performed by means of a vast number of fibres,
or teeth, which the laminae shoot forth on each side and which
hook and grapple together. A friend of mine counted fifty of
these fibres in one twentieth of an inch. These fibres are

crooked, but curved after a different manner. Those which proceed from the thread on the side towards the extremity of the feather, are longer, more flexible, and bent downward. Whereas those which proceed from the sides towards the beginning, or quill-end of the feather, are shorter, firmer, and turn upwards. The process then which takes place is as follows: When two laminae are pressed together, so that these long fibres are forced far enough over the short ones, their crooked parts fall into the cavity made by the crooked parts of the others – just as the latch that is fastened to a door enters into the cavity of the catch fixed to the doorpost, and there hooking itself, fastens the door. It is in this manner that one thread of a feather is fastened to the other.

This admirable structure of the feather, which it is easy to see with the microscope, succeeds perfectly for the use to which nature has designed it. Which use was not only that the laminae might be united, but that when one thread or lamina has been separated from another by some external violence, it might be reclasped with sufficient facility and expedition. In the ostrich, this apparatus of crochet and fibres, or hooks and teeth, is wanting – and we see the consequences of the want! The filaments hang loose and separate from one another, forming only a kind of down. Which constitution of the feathers, however it may fit them for the honours of a lady's head-dress, may be reckoned an imperfection in the bird, inasmuch as wings composed of these feathers, although they may assist it in running, do not serve for flight!

But under the present division of our subject, our business with feathers is as they are the covering of the bird. And herein a singular circumstance occurs. In the small order of birds which winter with us, from a snipe downwards, let the external colour of the feathers be what it will, their Creator has universally given them a bed of *black* down next [to] their bodies. Black, we know, is the warmest colour, and the purpose here is to keep in the heat arising from the heart and circulation of the blood. It is further likewise remarkable that this is *not* found in larger birds, for which there is also a reason – small birds are much more exposed to the cold than large ones, forasmuch as they present, in proportion to their bulk, a much larger surface to the air. If a turkey were divided into a number of wrens (supposing the shape of the turkey and the wren to be similar), the surface of all the wrens would exceed the surface of the turkey in the proportion of ten to one! It was necessary, therefore, that small birds should be more warmly clad than large ones.

* * * * *

In comparing the bones of different animals, we are struck, in the bones of birds, with a propriety which could only proceed from the wisdom of an intelligent and designing Creator. In the bones of an animal which is to fly, the two qualities required are strength and lightness. Wherein, therefore, do the bones of birds (I speak of the cylindrical bones) differ in these respects from the bones of quadrupeds? In three properties. First, their cavities are much larger in proportion to the weight of the bone than in those quadrupeds. Secondly, these cavities are empty. [And] thirdly, the shell is of a firmer texture than is the substance of other bones. Now, the weight being the same, the diameter, it is evident, will be greater in a hollow bone than in a solid one, and with the diameter, as every mathematician can prove, is increased the strength of the cylinder, or its resistance to breaking. In a word, a bone of the same weight would not have been so strong in any other form, and to have made it heavier would have incommoded the animal's flight. Yet this form could not be acquired by use or by exercise. What appetency could excavate a bone?

The lungs also of birds, as compared with the lungs of quadrupeds, contain in them a provision distinguishingly calculated for this same purpose of levitation, namely a communication (not found in other kinds of animals) between the air-vessels of the lungs and the cavities of the body, so that by the intromission of air from one to another (at the will, it should seem, of the animal), its body can be occasionally puffed out, and its tendency to descend in the air, or its specific gravity, made less. The bodies of birds are blown up from their lungs (which no other animal bodies are) and thus rendered buoyant!

All birds are oviparous. This, likewise, carries on the work of gestation with as little increase as possible of the weight of the body. A gravid uterus would have been a troublesome burden to a bird in its flight. The advantage in this respect of an oviparous procreation is, that whilst the whole brood are hatched together, the eggs are excluded singly, and at considerable intervals. Ten, fifteen, or twenty young birds may be produced in one clutch, yet the parent have never been encumbered by the load of more than one full-grown egg at one time!

✳ ✳ ✳ ✳ ✳

A principal topic of comparison between animals is their instruments of motion. These come before us under three divisions: feet, wings and fins. I desire any man to say which of the three is best fitted for its use, or whether the same consummate art be not conspicuous in them all.

The constitution of the elements in which the motion is to be performed, is very different. The animal action must necessarily follow that constitution. The Creator, therefore, if we might so speak, had to prepare for different situations, [and] for different difficulties. Yet the purpose is accomplished not less successfully in one case than in the other. And between wings and the corresponding limbs of quadrupeds, it is accomplished without deserting the general idea!

The idea is modified, not deserted. Strip a wing of its feathers, and it bears no obscure resemblance to the fore-leg of a quadruped. The articulations at the shoulder and the cubitus are much alike, and, what is closer to circumstance, in both cases the upper part of the limb consists of a single bone, the lower part of two. But, fitted up with its furniture of feathers and quills, it becomes a wonderful instrument more artificial than its first appearance indicates, though that be very striking! At least, the use which the bird makes of its wings in flying, is more complicated and more curious than is generally known.

One thing is certain, that if the flapping of the wings in flight were no more than the reciprocal motion of the same surface in opposite directions, either up or down, the bird would loose as much by one motion as she gained by another. The skylark could never ascend by such an action as this, for though the stroke upon the air by the under-side of her wing would carry her up, the stroke from the upper-side when she raised her wing again, would bring her down. In order, therefore, to account for the advantage which the bird derives from her wing, it is necessary to suppose that the surface of the wing is contracted while the wing is drawn up, and let out to its full expansion when it descends. Now, the form and structure of the wing, its external convexity, the disposition and particularly the overlapping of its larger feathers, the action of the muscles and joints of the pinions, are all adapted to this alternate adjustment of its shape and dimensions. Such a twist is given to the great feathers of the wing that they strike the air with their flat side, but rise from the stroke slantwise. The turning of the oar in rowing whilst the rower advances his hand for a new stroke, is a similar operation to that of the feather, and takes its name from the resemblance. I believe that this faculty is not found in the great feathers of the tail.

This is the place also for observing that the pinions are so set upon the body as to bring down the wings not vertically, but in a direction obliquely tending towards the tail. Which motion does two things at the same time – supports the body in the air, and carries it forward. The steerage of a bird in its flight is effected partly by the wings, but in a principal degree by the tail. And herein we meet with a circumstance not a little remarkable. Birds with long legs, have short tails, and in their flight [they] place their legs close to their bodies, at the same time stretching them out backwards as far as they can. In this position, the legs extend beyond the rump and become the rudder, supplying that steerage which the tail could not!

From the wings of birds, the transition is easy to the fins of fish. They are both, to their respective tribes, the instruments of their motion. But, in the work that they have to do, there is a considerable difference founded in this circumstance:

Fish, unlike birds, have very nearly the same specific gravity with the element in which they move. In the case of fish, therefore, there is little or no weight to bear up. What is wanted is only an impulse sufficient to carry the body through a resisting medium, or to maintain the posture, or to support or restore the balance of the body, which is always the most unsteady when there is no weight to sink it. For these offices the fins are as large as necessary, though much smaller than wings, [but] their action [is] in the highest degree convenient.

Regarding animals in their instruments of motion, [and] if it were our intention to pursue the consideration further, I should take in that generic distinction amongst birds, the web-foot of water-fowl. It is an instance which may be pointed out to a child. The utility of the web to water-fowl, [and] the inutility to land-fowl, are so obvious that it seems impossible to notice the difference without acknowledging the design. I am at a loss to know how those who deny the agency of an intelligent Creator, dispose of this example. There is nothing in the action of swimming, as carried on by a bird upon the surface of the water, that should generate a membrane between the toes. It is an exercise of constant resistance! The web-feet of amphibious quadrupeds, seals, otters &c, fall under the same observation.

✳ ✳ ✳ ✳ ✳

The five senses are common to most large animals. Nor have we much difference to remark in their constitution. The superior sagacity of animals which hunt their prey, and which consequently depend for their livelihood upon their nose, is well known in its use, but not at all known in the organisation which produces it.

The external ears of beasts of prey, of lions, tigers, wolves, have their trumpet-part standing forwards to seize the sounds which are before them, of the animals which they pursue or watch. The ears of animals in flight are turned backwards to

123

give notice of the approach of their enemy from behind, whence he may steal upon them unseen. This is a critical distinction!

The eyes of animals which follow their prey by night, as cats, owls &c, possess a faculty not given to those of other species, namely of closing the pupil entirely! The final cause of which seems to be this: It was necessary for such animals to descry objects with very small degrees of light. This capacity depended upon the superior sensibility of the retina, that is, upon its being affected by the most feeble impulses. But that tenderness of structure which rendered the membrane exquisitely sensible, rendered it also liable to be offended by the access of stronger degrees of light. The contractile range, therefore, of the pupil is increased in these animals so as to enable them to close the aperture entirely, which includes the power of diminishing it in every degree whereby at all times such portions [of light] are admitted as may be received without injury to the sense.

There appears to be also in the figure, and in some properties, of the pupil of the eye, an appropriate relation to the wants of different animals. In horses, oxen, goats, [and] sheep, the pupil of the eye is elliptical, the transverse axis being horizontal. By which structure, although the eye be placed on the side of the head, the anterior elongation of the pupil catches the forward rays, or those which come from objects immediately in front of the animal's face.

Chapter Thirteen

All the [following] instances might consistently enough with language, have been placed under the head of Comparative Anatomy. But there appears to me an impropriety in the use which that term hath obtained, it being in some sort absurd to call that a case of comparative anatomy in which there is nothing to compare – in which a conformation is found in one animal, which hath nothing properly answering it in another. Of this kind are the examples which I have to propose in the present chapter, and the reader will see that they must necessarily be of a miscellaneous nature. To dispose them into some sort of order, we will notice first [some] particularities of structure which belong to quadrupeds, birds and fish, or to many kinds included in these classes of animals, and then such particularities as are confined to one or two species.

Along each side of the neck of large quadrupeds, runs a stiff, robust cartilage which butchers call the pax-wax. No person can carve the upper end of a crop of beef without driving his knife against it. It is a tough, strong, tendinous substance braced from the head to the middle of the back. Its office is to assist in supporting the weight of the head. It is a mechanical provision and sufficient for the purpose which it has to execute. The head of an ox or a horse is a heavy weight, acting at the end of a long lever (consequently with great purchase), and in a direction nearly perpendicular to the joints of the supporting neck. From such a force, so advantageously applied, the bones of the neck would be in constant danger of dislocation if they were not fortified by this strong tape. No such organ is found in the human subject because from the erect position of the head (the pressure of it acting nearly in the direction of the spine), the junction of the vertebrae appears to be sufficiently secure without it. This cautionary expedient, therefore, is limited to quadrupeds, [and] the care of the Creator is seen where it is wanted.

The oil with which birds prune their feathers, and the organ which supplies it, is a specific provision of the winged creation. On each side of the rump of birds is observed a small nipple yielding upon pressure a butter-like substance, which the bird extracts by pinching the pap with its bill. With this oil thus procured, the bird dresses its coat and repeats the action as often as its own sensations teach it that it is in any part wanted. The gland, the pap, the nature and quality of the excreted substance, the manner of obtaining it, the application of it when obtained, form an evidence of intention which is not easy to withstand. Nothing similar to it is found in unfeathered animals. What blind conatus of nature should produce it in birds, [but] should not produce it in beasts?

The air-bladder also of a fish affords a plain and direct instance of contrivance. The principle of the contrivance is clear. The use of the organ to sustain and also elevate the body of the fish in water is proved by observing that flounders, soles [and] skates, which are without the air-bladder, seldom rise in the water, and that with effort. The manner in which the purpose is attained, and the suitableness of the means to the end, are not difficult to be apprehended. The rising and sinking of a fish in water, so far as it is independent of the stroke of the fins and tail, can only be regulated by the specific gravity of the body. When the bladder contained in the body of the fish is contracted, which the fish possesses a muscular power of doing, the bulk of the fish is contracted along with it. Whereby, since the absolute weight remains the same, the specific gravity, which is the sinking force, is increased and the fish descends. On the contrary, when in consequence of the relaxation of the muscles, the elasticity of the enclosed and now compressed air restores the dimensions of the bladder, the tendency downwards becomes proportionably less than it was before, or is turned into a contrary tendency.

These are known properties of bodies immersed in a fluid. The enamelled figures or little glass bubbles in a jar of water, are made to rise and fall by the same artifice. A diving-machine might be made to ascend and descend upon the like principle, namely by introducing into the inside of it an air-vessel which, by its contraction, would diminish, and by its distension would enlarge the bulk of the machine itself, and thus render it specifically heavier or specifically lighter than the water which surrounds it. Suppose this to be done, and the artist to solicit a patent for his invention. The inspectors of the model, whatever they might think of the use or value of the contrivance, could by no possibility entertain a question in their minds whether it were a contrivance or not. No reason has ever been assigned – no reason *can* be assigned – why the conclusion is not as certain in the fish as it is in the machine, [or] why the argument is not as firm in one case as the other!

It would be very worthy of enquiry if it were possible to discover by what method an animal, which lives constantly in water, is able to supply a repository of air. The expedient, whatever it be, forms part, and perhaps the most curious part of the provision. Nothing similar to the air-bladder is found in land-animals, and a life in the water has no natural tendency to produce a bag of air. Nothing can be further from an acquired organisation than this is. These examples mark the attention of the Creator to the three great kingdoms of His animal creation.

The example which stands next in point of generality, is the poisonous tooth of serpents. The fang of a viper is a clear and curious example of contrivance. It is a perforated tooth, loose at the root, in its quiet state lying down flat upon the jaw, but furnished with a muscle which, with a jerk and by the pluck, as it were, of a string, suddenly erects it. Under the tooth, close to its root and communicating with the perforation, lies a small bag containing the venom. When the fang is raised, the closing of the jaw presses its root against the bag underneath, and the force of this compression sends out the fluid with a consider-able impetus through the tube in the middle of the tooth. What more unequivocal or effectual apparatus could be devised for the double purpose of at once inflicting the wound and injecting the poison? Yet, though lodged in the mouth, it is so constituted as in its inoffensive and quiescent state not to interfere with the animal's ordinary office of receiving its food. It has been observed also that none of the harmless serpents have these fangs, but teeth of an equal size fixed into the jaw.

That which I shall next mention is the bag of the opossum. This is a mechanical contrivance properly so called. The simplicity of the expedient renders the contrivance more obvious than many others, and by no means less certain. A false skin under the belly of the animal forms a pouch into which the young litter are received at their birth, where they have an easy access to the teats [and] in which they are transported from place to place, where they are at liberty to run in and out, and where they find a refuge from surprise and danger. It is their cradle, their asylum, and the machine for their conveyance. Can the use of this structure be doubted of? Nor is it a mere doubling of the skin, but a new organ, furnished with bones and muscles of its own. Two bones are placed before the os pubis, and [are] joined to that bone as their base. These support and give fixture to the muscles which serve to open the bag. To these muscles there are antagonists which serve in the same manner to shut it. And this office they perform so exactly, that in the living animal the opening can scarcely be discerned except when forcibly drawn asunder. Is there any action in this part of the animal, [or] any process arising from that action, by which these members could be formed? [Can] any account be given of the formation except design?

As a particularity, yet appertaining to more species than one, we may notice a circumstance in the structure of the claws of certain birds. The middle claw of the heron and cormorant, is toothed and notched like a saw. These birds are great fishers, and these notches assist them in holding their slippery prey. The use is evident, but the structure such as cannot at all be accounted for by the effort of the animal or the exercise of the part. Some other fishing birds have these notches in their bills, and for the same purpose. The gannet, or Soland goose, has the side of its bill irregularly jagged so that it may hold its prey the faster. Nor can the structure in this, more than in the former case, arise from the manner of employing the part. The smooth surfaces and soft flesh of fish were less likely to notch the bills of birds than the hard bodies upon which many other species feed.

* * * * *

We now come to particularities, strictly so called, as being limited to a single species of animal. Of these, I shall take one from a quadruped and one from a bird:

The stomach of the camel is well known to retain large quantities of water, and to retain it unchanged for a considerable length of time. This property qualifies it for living in the desert. Let us see, therefore, what is the internal organisation upon which a faculty so rare and so beneficial depends.

A number of distinct sacs or bags (in a dromedary thirty of these have been counted) are observed to lie between the membranes of the second stomach, and to open into the stomach near the top by small square apertures. Through these orifices, after the stomach is full, the annexed bags are filled, and the water so deposited is, in the first place, not liable to pass into the intestines, in the second place is kept separate from the solid aliment, and in the third place is out of the reach of the digestive action of the stomach. It appears certain that the animal possesses the power of squeezing back this water from the adjacent bags into the stomach whenever thirst excites it to put this power into action.

The tongue of the woodpecker is one of those singularities which nature presents us with when a singular purpose is to be answered. It is a particular instrument for a particular use, and what except design ever produces such? The woodpecker lives chiefly upon insects lodged in the bodies of decayed or decaying trees. For the purpose of boring into the wood, it is furnished with a bill [that is] straight, hard, angular and sharp. When by means of this it has reached the cells of the insects, then comes the office of its tongue, which tongue is first of such a length that the bird can dart it three or four inches from the bill – in this respect differing from every other species of bird. In the second place, it is tipped with a stiff, sharp, bony thorn. And in the third place (which appears to me the most remarkable property of all), this tip is dentated on both sides like the beard of an arrow or the barb of a hook. The description of the part declares its uses. The bird, having exposed the retreats of the insects by the assistance of its bill, with a motion inconceivably quick, launches out at them this long tongue, transfixes them upon the barbed needle at the end of it, and thus draws its prey within its mouth. If this be not a mechanism, what is?

Should it be said that by continual endeavours to shoot out the tongue at the stretch, the woodpecker's species may by degrees have lengthened the organ itself beyond that of other birds, what account can be given of its form, [or] of its tip? How, in particular, did it get its barb? These barbs, in my opinion, wherever they occur, are decisive proofs of mechanical contrivance.

I shall add one more example for the sake of its novelty. It is always an agreeable discovery when, having remarked in an animal an extraordinary structure, we come at length to find an unexpected use for it. The following narrative furnishes an instance of this kind. The babyrouessa, or Indian hog, a species of wild boar found in the East Indies, has two bent teeth more than half a yard long, growing upwards (which is the singularity) from the *upper* jaw. These instruments are not wanted for offence, that service being provided for by two tusks issuing from the upper jaw, and resembling those of the common boar. Nor does the animal use them for defence. They might seem, therefore, to be a superfluity and an encumbrance. But observe the event – The animal sleeps *standing*, and in order to support its head, hooks its upper tusks upon the branches of trees!

Chapter Fourteen

I can hardly imagine to myself a more distinguishing mark, and consequently a more certain proof of design, than *preparation*, i.e. the providing of things beforehand which are not to be used until a considerable time afterwards. For this implies a contemplation of the future, which belongs only to intelligence. Of these respective contrivances, the bodies of animals furnish various examples.

Human teeth afford an instance not only of prospective contrivance, but of the completion of the contrivance being designedly suspended. They are formed within the gums, and there they stop – the fact being that their further advance to maturity would not only be useless to the new-born [infant], but in its way! It is evident that the act of sucking by which it is for some time to be nourished, will be performed with more ease both to the nurse and to the infant whilst the inside of the mouth and edges of the gums are smooth and soft, than if set with hard, pointed [teeth]. By the time they *are* wanted, the teeth are ready. They have been lodged within the gums for some months past, but detained so long as their further protrusion would interfere with the office to which the mouth is destined. Nature, namely that intelligence which was employed in creation, looked beyond the first year of the infant's life. Yet, whilst she was providing for functions which were to become necessary, was careful not to incommode those which preceded them.

What renders it more probable that this is the effect of design, is that the teeth are imperfect whilst all other parts of the mouth are perfect. The lips are perfect. The tongue is perfect. The cheeks, the jaws, the palate, the pharynx, the larynx, are all perfect. The teeth alone are not so.

When a contrary order is necessary, a contrary order prevails. In the worm of the beetle as hatched from the egg, the teeth are the first things which arrive at perfection. The insect begins to gnaw as soon as it escapes from the shell, though its other parts be only gradually advancing to their maturity!

What has been observed of the teeth is true of the horns of animals, and for the same reason. The horn of a calf or a lamb does not bud, or at least does not sprout to any considerable length, until the animal be capable of browsing upon its pasture, because such a substance upon the forehead of the young animal would very much incommode the teat in the office of giving suck.

But in the case of teeth, of human teeth at least, the prospective contrivance looks still further. A succession of crops is provided, and provided from the beginning, a second tier [of teeth] being originally formed beneath the first, which do not come into use till several years afterwards. And this double, or suppletory, provision meets a difficulty in the mechanism of the mouth which would have appeared almost insurmountable. The expansion of the jaw (the consequence of the growth of the [infant] and of its skull) necessarily separates the teeth of the first set, however compactly disposed, to a distance from one another, which would be very inconvenient. In due time, therefore, i.e. when the jaw has attained a great part of its dimensions, a new set of teeth springs up (loosening and pushing out the old ones before them), more exactly fitted to the space which they are to occupy, and rising also in such close ranks as to allow for any extension of line which the subsequent enlargement of the head may occasion.

✳ ✳ ✳ ✳ ✳

It is not very easy to conceive a more evidently prospective contrivance than that which, in all viviparous animals, is found in the milk of the female parent. At the moment the young animal enters the world, there is its maintenance ready for it. The particulars to be remarked in this economy are neither few nor slight. We have first the nutritious quality of the fluid, unlike in this respect every other excretion of the body, and in which nature remains hitherto unimitated, neither cookery nor chemistry having been able to make milk out of grass.

We have secondly the organ for its reception and retention. We have thirdly the excretory duct annexed to that organ. And we have lastly the determination of the milk to the breast at the particular juncture when it is about to be wanted. We have all these properties in the subject before us, and they are all indications of design. The last circumstance is the strongest of any.

The lacteal system is a constant wonder, and it adds to other causes of our admiration that the number of teats or paps in each species is found to bear a proportion to the number of young. In the sow, the bitch, the rabbit, the cat, the rat, which have numerous litters, the paps are numerous and are disposed along the whole length of the belly. In the cow and mare they are few. The most simple account of this is to refer it to a designing Creator.

✳ ✳ ✳ ✳ ✳

But, in the argument before us, we are entitled to consider not only animal bodies when framed, but the circumstances under which they are framed. And in this view of the subject the constitution of many of their parts is most strictly prospective.

The eye is of no use at the time when it is formed. It is an optical instrument made in a dungeon, constructed for the refraction of light to a focus, and perfect for its purpose before a ray of light has had access to it, geometrically adapted to the properties and action of an element with which it has no communication. And this is precisely the thing which evidences intention. It is providing for the future in the closest sense which can be given to these terms. It is providing for a future change, not for the then-subsisting condition of the animal,

133

not for any gradual progress or advance in that same condition, but for a new state, the consequence of a great and sudden alteration which the animal is to undergo at its birth. Is it to be believed that the eye was formed, or the series of causes was fixed by which the eye is formed, without a view to this change? [Or] without a prospect of that condition in which its fabric, of no use at present, is about to be of the greatest [utility], without a consideration of the qualities of that element with which it was hereafter to hold so intimate a relation? Could this be done without a *reasoning* mind? The eye formed in one state for use in another, and in a *different* state, affords proof of destination to a future purpose, and a proof proportionably stronger as the machinery is more complicated and the adaptation more exact!

What has been said of the eye, holds equally true of the lungs. Composed of air-vessels where there is no air, elaborately constructed for the alternate admission and expulsion of an elastic fluid where no such fluid exists, this great organ, with the whole apparatus belonging to it, lies collapsed in the foetal thorax, yet in order and readiness for action the first moment the occasion requires its service! This is having a machine locked up for future use, which incontestably proves that the case was expected to occur in which this use might be experienced. But expectation is the proper act of intelligence. Considering the state in which an animal exists before its birth, [finding] a system of lungs is like finding a pair of bellows in the bottom of the sea – of no sort of use in the situation in which they are found, formed for an action which was impossible to be exerted, but [suited] to another element in another place.

As part and parcel of the same plan ought to be mentioned, in speaking of the lungs, the provisionary contrivances of the foramen ovale and ductus arteriosus. In the foetus, pipes are laid for the passage of the blood through the lungs. But, until the lungs be inflated by the inspiration of air, that passage is impervious, or in a great degree obstructed. What then is to be done? What would an artist, what would a *master* do upon the occasion? He would endeavour, most probably, to provide a temporary passage which might carry the communication required until the other was open. Now, this is the thing which is actually done – in the heart! Instead of the circuitous route through the lungs which the blood afterwards takes before it gets from one auricle of the heart to the other, a portion of the blood passes immediately from the right auricle to the left through a hole placed in the partition which separates these cavities. This hole anatomists call the foramen ovale.

There is likewise another cross-cut answering the same purpose by what is called the ductus arteriosus, lying between the pulmonary artery and the aörta. But both expedients are so strictly temporary that after birth the one passage is closed, and the tube which forms the other [is] shrivelled up into a ligament! If *this* be not contrivance, what is?

But, forasmuch as the action of the air upon the blood in the lungs appears to be necessary to the perfect life and health of the animal (otherwise the shortest route might still be the best), how comes it to pass that the foetus lives and grows and thrives without it? The answer is, that the blood of the foetus is the mother's – that it has undergone that action in her habit [so] that one pair of lungs serves for both! When the animals are separated, a new necessity arises, and to meet this necessity as soon as it occurs an organisation is prepared. It is ready for its purpose. It only waits for the atmosphere, [and] it begins to play the moment the air is admitted to it.

Chapter Fifteen

When several different parts contribute to one effect, the fitness of such parts to one another is what I call 'relation'. And wherever this is observed in the works of nature or of man, it appears to me to carry along with it decisive evidence of understanding, intention [and] art. In examining, for instance, the several parts of a watch, the spring, the barrel, the chain, the fusee, the balance, the wheels of various sizes, [their] forms and positions, what is it which would take an observer's attention as most plainly evincing a construction directed by thought, deliberation and contrivance?

It is the *suitableness* of these parts to one another, first in the succession and order in which they act, and secondly the effect finally produced. Thus, referring the spring to the wheels, our observer sees in it that which originates and upholds their motion, in the chain that which transmits the motion to the fusee which communicates it to the wheels. In the conical figure of the fusee, if he refer to the spring, he sees that which corrects the inequality of its force. Referring the wheels to one another, he notices first their teeth, which would have been without use or meaning if there had been only one wheel, or if the wheels had had no common bearing upon some joint effect. Secondly, the correspondency of their position so that the teeth of one wheel catch into the teeth of another. Thirdly, the proportion observed in the number of teeth of each wheel, which determines the rate of going. Referring the balance to the rest of the works, he saw that which rendered their motions equable. [And] lastly, in looking upon the index and face of the watch, he saw the use and conclusion of the mechanism marking the succession of minutes and hours, but all depending upon the motions within [and] upon the system of intermediate actions between the spring and the pointer.

What thus struck his attention in the several parts of the watch, he might designate by one name of 'relation'. And observing with respect to all cases whatever in which the origin and formation of a thing could be ascertained by evidence – that these relations were found in things produced by art and design and in no other things – he would rightly deem them [to be] characteristic of such productions, [and] apply the reasoning here described to the works of nature, [for] the animal economy is full of these relations.

The relation of the kidneys to the bladder, and of the ureters to both, i.e. of the secreting organ to the vessel receiving the secreted liquor, and the pipe laid from one to the other for the purpose of conveying it, is as manifest as it is amongst the different vessels employed in a distillery. The structure in this case is capable of being apprehended by every understanding – this correlation fixes intention *somewhere*!

If the bladder [as some say] had been merely an expansion of the ureter produced by retention of the fluid, there ought to have been a bladder for *each* ureter! One receptacle fed by two pipes issuing from different sides of the body, yet from both conveying the same fluid, is not to be accounted for by any such supposition as this.

Relation of parts to one another accompanies us throughout the whole animal economy. Can any relation be more simple, yet more convincing than this, that the eyes are so placed as to look in the direction in which the legs move and the hands work? It might have happened very differently if it had been left to chance. There were, at least, three quarters of the compass out of four to have erred in. Any considerable alteration in the position of the eye, or the figure of the joints, would have disturbed the line and destroyed the alliance between the sense and the limbs.

But relation, perhaps, is never so striking as when it subsists not between different parts of the same thing, but between different things. The relation between a lock and a key is more obvious than it is between different parts of the lock. A bow was designed for an arrow, and an arrow for a bow, and the design is more evident for their being separate implements. Nor do the works of the Deity want this clearest species of relation. The sexes are manifestly made for each other. They form the grandest relation of animated nature, universal, organic, mechanical, subsisting like the clearest relations of art in different individuals, unequivocal, [and] inexplicable [if] without design. So much so that, were every other proof of contrivance in nature dubious or obscure, this alone would be sufficient. The example is complete. Nothing is wanting in the argument, [and] I see no way whatever of getting over it.

These are general relations. Particular relations are such as the following:

In the swan, the web-foot, the spoon-bill, the long neck, the thick down, the graminivorous stomach, bear all a relation to one another inasmuch as they all concur in one design, that of supplying the occasions of an aquatic fowl floating upon the surface of shallow pools of water, and seeking its food at the bottom. Begin with any one of these particularities of structure, and observe how the rest follow it. The web-foot qualifies the bird for swimming, the spoon-bill enables it to graze. But how is an animal, floating upon the surface, to graze at the bottom except by the mediation of a long neck? A long neck, accordingly, is given to it.

Again, a warm-blooded animal which was to pass its life upon water required a defence against the coldness of that element. Such a defence is furnished to the swan in the muff in which its body is wrapped. But all this outward apparatus would have been in vain if the intestinal system had not been suited to the digestion of vegetable substances.

I say suited to the digestion of vegetable substances, for it is well known that there are two intestinal systems found in birds, one with a membranous stomach and a gastric juice capable of dissolving animal substances alone, [and] the other with a crop and gizzard calculated for the moistening, bruising and afterwards digesting of vegetable aliment.

Or set off with any other distinctive part in the body of the swan – for instance, with the long neck. The long neck, without the web-foot, would have been an encumbrance to the bird. Yet there is no necessary connection between a long neck and a web-foot. In fact, they do not usually go together. How happens it, therefore, that they meet only when a particular design demands the aid of both?

This mutual relation arising from a subserviency to a common purpose is very much observable also in the parts of a mole. The strong short legs of that animal, the palmated feet armed with sharp nails, the pig-like nose, the teeth, the velvet coat, the small external ear, the sagacious smell, the sunk protected eye, all conduce to the utilities or to the safety of its underground life. It is a special purpose, specially consulted throughout.

The form of the feet fixes the character of the animal. They are so many shovels. They determine its action to that of rooting in the ground, and everything about its body agrees with this destination. The cylindrical figure of the mole, as well as the compactness of its form arising from the terseness of its limbs, proportionably lessens its labour, because according to its bulk, it thereby requires the least possible quantity of earth to be removed for its progress.

It has nearly the same structure of the face and jaws of a swine, and the same office for them. The nose is sharp, slender, tendinous, strong, with a pair of nerves going down to the end of it. The plush covering which, by the smoothness, closeness, and polish of the short piles that compose it, rejects the adhesion of almost every species of earth. [It] defends the animal from cold and wet, and from the impediment which it would experience by mould sticking to its body. From soils of all kinds the little pioneer comes forth bright and clean. Inhabiting dirt, it is of all animals the neatest!

But what I have always most admired in the mole is its eyes. This animal, occasionally visiting the surface, and wanting for its safety and direction to be informed when it does so, or when it approaches it, a perception of light was necessary. I do not know that the clearness of sight depends at all upon the size of the organ. What is gained by the largeness or prominence of the globe of the eye is width in the field of vision. Such a capacity would be of no use to an animal which was to seek its food in the dark. The mole did not want to look about it. Nor would a large advanced eye have been easily defended from the annoyance to which the life of the animal must constantly expose it. How, indeed, was the mole, working its way underground, to guard its eyes at all?

In order to meet this difficulty, the eyes are made scarcely larger than the head of a corking-pin. And these minute globules are sunk so deeply in the skull, and lie so sheltered within the velvet of its covering, that any contraction of what may be called the eye-brows not only closes up the apertures which lead to the eyes, but presents a cushion, as it were, to any sharp or protruding substance which might push against them. This aperture, even in its ordinary state, is like a pin-hole in a piece of velvet, scarcely pervious to loose particles of earth.

Observe then in this structure that which we call relation. There is no natural connexion between a small sunk eye and a shovel palmated foot. Palmated feet might have been joined with goggle-eyes, or small eyes might have been joined with feet of any other form. What was it, therefore, which brought them together in the mole? That which brought together the barrel, the chain, and the fusee in a watch – design! And design [which was] in both cases inferred from the relation which the parts bear to one another in the prosecution of a common purpose!

As hath already been observed, there are different ways of stating the relation according as we set out from a different part. In the instance before us, we may either consider the shape of the feet as qualifying the animal for that mode of life to which the structure of its eyes confine it. Or we may consider the structure of the eye as the only one which would have suited with the action to which the feet are adapted. The relation is manifest whichever of the parts related we place first in the order of our consideration. In a word, the feet of the mole are made for digging, [and] the neck, nose, eyes, ears and skin are peculiarly adapted to an underground life. And this is what I call relation.

Chapter Sixteen

Compensation is a species of relation. It is relation when the defects of one part are supplied by the structure of another. Thus, the short unbending neck of an elephant is compensated by the length and flexibility of his proboscis. He could not have reached the ground without it. Or, if it be supposed that he might have fed upon the fruit of trees, how was he to drink? Should it be asked, 'Why is the elephant's neck so short?', it may be answered that the weight of a head so heavy could not have been supported at the end of a longer lever. To a form, therefore, in some respects necessary, but in some respects also inadequate to the occasion of the animal, a supplement is added which exactly makes up the deficiency under which he laboured.

If it be suggested that this proboscis may have been produced in a long course of generations by the constant endeavour of the elephant to thrust out his nose (which is the general hypothesis by which it has lately been attempted to account for the forms of animated nature), I would ask, how was the animal to subsist in the meantime during this process, until this prolongation of snout were completed? What was to become of the individual whilst the species was perfecting?

Our business at present is simply to point out the relation which this organ bears to the peculiar figure of the animal to which it belongs. Herein all things correspond. The necessity of the elephant's proboscis arises from the shortness of his neck, [and] the shortness of the neck is rendered necessary by the weight of the head. Were we to enter into an examination of the structure and anatomy of the proboscis itself, we should see in it one of the most curious of all examples of animal mechanism. The disposition of the ringlets and fibres for the purpose, first, of forming a long cartilaginous pipe, secondly of contracting and lengthening that pipe, thirdly of turning it in every direction at the will of the animal, with the superaddition at the end of a fleshy production of about the length and thickness of a finger, and performing the office of a finger so as to pick up a straw from the ground – these properties of the same organ, taken together, exhibit a specimen not only of design (which is attested by the advantage), but of consummate art and elaborate preparation in accomplishing that design!

The hook in the wing of a bat is strictly a mechanical, and also a compensating, contrivance. At the angle of its wing there is a bent claw exactly in the form of a hook, by which the bat attaches itself to the sides of rocks, caves and buildings, laying hold of crevices, joinings, chinks and roughnesses. It hooks itself by this claw, remains suspended by this hold, [and] takes its flight from this position, which operations compensate for the decrepitude of its legs and feet. Without her hook, the bat would be the most helpless of animals. She can neither run upon her feet nor raise herself from the ground. These inabilities are made up to her by the contrivance in her wing. And in placing a claw in that part, the Creator has deviated from the analogy observed in winged animals – a singular defect required a singular substitute!

The crane-kind are to live and seek their food amongst the waters, yet, having no web-feet, are incapable of swimming. To make up for this deficiency, they are furnished with long legs for wading, or long bills for groping, or usually with both. This is compensation. But I think the true reflection upon the present instance is how every part of nature is tenanted by appropriate inhabitants. Not only is the surface of deep waters peopled by numerous tribes of birds that swim, but marshes and shallow pools are furnished with hardly less numerous tribes of birds that wade.

The common parrot has in the structure of its beak both an inconveniency and a compensation for it. When I speak of an inconveniency, I have a view to a dilemma which frequently occurs in the works of nature, [namely] that the peculiarity of structure by which an organ is made to answer one purpose, necessarily unfits it for another purpose. This is the case before us. The upper bill of the parrot is so much hooked, and so much overlaps the lower, that if, as in other birds, the lower chap alone had motion, the bird could scarcely gape wide enough to receive its food. Yet this hook and overlapping of the bill could not be spared, for it forms the very instrument by which the bird climbs – to say nothing of the use which it makes of it in breaking nuts and the hard substances upon which it feeds. How, therefore, has nature provided for the opening of this occluded mouth? – by making the upper chap moveable as well as the lower. In most birds, the upper chap is connected, and makes but one piece with the skull. But in the parrot the upper chap is joined to the bone of the head by a strong membrane placed on each side of it, which lifts and depresses it at pleasure.

The spider's web is a compensating contrivance. The spider lives upon flies [but is] without wings to pursue them, a case, one would have thought, of great difficulty – yet provided for, and provided for by a resource which no stratagem, no effort of the animal, could have produced had not both its external and internal structure been specifically adapted to the operation.

In many species of insects, the eye is fixed, and consequently without the power of turning the pupil to the object. This great defect is, however, perfectly compensated, and by a mechanism which we should not suspect. The eye is a multiplying glass, with a lens looking in every direction and catching every object. By which means, although the orb of the eye be stationary, the field of vision is as ample as that of other animals and is commanded on every side. When this lattice-work was first observed, the multiplicity and minuteness of the surfaces must have added to the surprise of the discovery.

Adams tells us that fourteen hundred of these reticulations have been counted in the two eyes of a drone-bee!

In other cases the compensation is effected by the number and position of the eyes themselves. The spider has eight eyes mounted upon different parts of the head, two in front, two in the top of the head, [and] two on each side. These eyes are without motion, but by their situation [are] suited to comprehend every view which the wants or safety of the animal render necessary.

The *Memoirs for the Natural History of Animals*, published by the French Academy, AD 1687, furnish us with some curious particulars in the eye of a chameleon. Instead of two eyelids, it is covered by an eyelid with a hole in it. This singular structure appears to be compensatory, and to answer to some other singularities in the shape of the animal. The neck of the chameleon is inflexible. To make up for this, the eye is so prominent that more than half the ball stands out of the head. By means of which extraordinary projection, the pupil of the eye can be carried by the muscles in every direction, and is capable of being pointed towards every object. But then, so unusual an exposure of the globe of the eye requires for its lubricity and defence, a more than ordinary protection of eyelid, as well as a more than ordinary supply of moisture. Yet the motion of an eyelid formed according to the common construction would be impeded, as it should seem, by the convexity of the organ. The aperture in the lid meets this difficulty. It enables the animal to keep the principal part of the surface of the eye under cover, and preserve it in a due state of humidity without shutting out the light, or without performing every moment a nictitation which, it is probable, would be more laborious to this animal than to others.

But the works of the Deity are known by expedients. Where we should look for absolute destitution, where we can reckon up nothing but wants, some contrivance always comes in to supply the privation. A snail, without wings, feet or thread, climbs up the stalks of plants by the sole aid of a viscid humour discharged from her skin. She adheres to the stems, leaves and fruits of plants by means of a sticking-plaster! A muscle, which might seem by its helplessness to lie at the mercy of every wave that went over it, has the singular power of spinning strong, tendinous threads by which she moors her shell to rocks and timbers. A cockle, on the contrary, by means of its stiff tongue, works for itself a shelter in the sand.

The provisions of nature extend to cases the most desperate. A lobster has in its constitution a difficulty so great that one could hardly conjecture beforehand how nature would dispose of it. In most animals, the skin grows with their growth. If, instead of a soft skin, there be a shell, still it admits of a gradual enlargement. If the shell, as in the tortoise, consist of several pieces, the accession of substance is made at the sutures. Bi-valve shells grow bigger by receiving an accretion at their edge. It is the same with spiral shells at their mouth. The simplicity of their form admits of this. But the lobster's shell being applied to the limbs of the body as well as to the body itself, allows not of either of the modes of growth which are observed to take place in other shells. Its hardness resists expansion, and its complexity renders it incapable of increasing its size by addition of substance to its edge. How then was the growth of the lobster to be provided for? Was room to be made for it in the old shell, or was it to be successively fitted with new ones? If a change of shell became necessary, how was the lobster to extricate himself from his present confinement? How was he to uncase his buckler, or draw his legs out of his boots?

The process, which fishermen have observed to take place, is as follows: At certain seasons, the shell of the lobster grows soft. The animal swells its body, the seams open and the claws burst at the joints. When the shell has thus become loose upon the body, the animal makes a second effort and, by a tremulous spasmodic motion, casts it off. In this state, the liberated but defenceless fish retires into holes in the rock. The released body now pushes its growth, [and] in about eight and forty hours a fresh concretion of humour upon the surface, i.e. a new shell, is formed, adapted in every part to the increased dimensions of the animal. This wonderful mutation is repeated every year.

147

If there be imputed defects without compensation, I should suspect that they were defects only in appearance. Thus, the body of the sloth has often been reproached for the slowness of its motions, which has been attributed to an imperfection in the formation of its limbs. But it ought to be observed that it is this slowness which alone suspends the voracity of the animal. He fasts during his migration from one tree to another, and this fast may be necessary for the relief of his over-charged vessels as well as to allow time for the concoction of the coarse and hard food which he has taken into his stomach. The tardiness of his pace seems to have reference to the capacity of his organs, and to his propensities with respect to food, i.e. is calculated to counteract the effects of repletion.

Or there may be cases in which a defect is artificial, and compensated by the very cause which produces it. Thus the sheep in the domesticated state in which we see it, is destitute of the ordinary means of defence or escape, [and] is incapable either of resistance or flight. But this is not so with the wild animal. The natural sheep is swift and active, and if it lose these qualities when it comes under the subjection of man, the loss is compensated by his protection. Perhaps there is no species of quadruped whatever which suffers so little as this does from the depredations of animals of prey!

* * * * *

For the sake of making our meaning better understood, we have considered this business of compensation under certain particularities of constitution in which it appears to be most conspicuous. This view of the subject necessarily limits the instances to single species of animals. But there are compensations, perhaps, not less certain which extend over large classes of living nature.

In quadrupeds, the deficiency of teeth is usually compensated by the faculty of rumination. The sheep, deer and ox tribe are without fore-teeth in the upper jaw. These ruminate. The horse and ass *are* furnished with [fore-]teeth in the upper jaw, and do not ruminate! In the former class, the grass and hay descend into the stomach nearly in the state in which they are cropped from the pasture. In the stomach, they are softened by the gastric juice, which in these animals is unusually copious. Thus softened and rendered tender, they are returned a second time to the action of the mouth where the grinding teeth complete at their leisure the trituration which is necessary, but which was before left imperfect. I say the trituration which is necessary, for it appears from experiments that the gastric fluid of sheep, for example, has no effect in digesting plants unless they have been previously masticated, that it only produces a slight maceration, nearly as common water would do in a like degree of heat, but that when once vegetables are reduced to pieces by mastication, the fluid then exerts upon them its specific operation. Its first effect is to soften them and to destroy their natural consistency. It then goes on to dissolve them, not sparing even the toughest parts, such as the nerves of the leaves. I think it very probable that the gratification also of the animal is renewed and prolonged by this faculty. Sheep, deer and oxen appear to be in state of enjoyment whilst they are chewing the cud. It is then, perhaps, that they best relish their food.

In birds the compensation is still more striking. They have no teeth at all. What have they then to make up for this severe want? I speak of granivorous and herbivorous birds such as common fowls, turkeys, ducks, geese, pigeons &c, for it is concerning these alone that the question need be asked.

All these are furnished with a peculiar and most powerful muscle called the gizzard, the inner coat of which is fitted up with rough plaits, which by a strong friction against one another, break and grind the hard aliment as effectually, and by the same mechanical action, as a coffee-mill would do. It has been proved by the most correct experiments that the gastric juice of these birds will not operate upon the entire grain, not even when softened with water or macerated in the crop. Therefore, without a grinding machine within its body, without the trituration of the gizzard, a chicken would have starved upon a heap of corn! Yet why should a bill and a gizzard go together? Why should a gizzard never be found where there are teeth?

Nor does the gizzard belong to birds as such. A gizzard is not found in birds of prey. Their food requires not to be ground down in a mill. The compensatory contrivance goes no further than the necessity. In both classes of birds, however, the digestive organ within the body bears a strict relation to the external instruments for procuring food. The soft membranous stomach accompanies a hooked, notched beak, short muscular legs, [and] strong, sharp, crooked talons. The cartilaginous stomach attends that conformation of bill and toes which restrains the bird to the picking of seeds or the cropping of plants.

But to proceed with our compensations. A very numerous tribe of terrestrial animals are entirely without feet, yet [are] locomotive, and in a very considerable degree swift in their motion. How is the want of feet compensated?

It is done by the disposition of the muscles and fibres of the trunk. In consequence of the collocation, and by means of the joint action of longitudinal and annular fibres, that is to say of strings and rings, the body and train of reptiles are capable of being reciprocally shortened and lengthened, drawn up and stretched out. The result of this action is a progressive, and in some cases, a rapid movement of the whole body in any direction to which the will of the animal determines it. The meanest creature is a collection of wonders!

The play of the rings in an earthworm as it crawls, the undulatory motion propogated along the body, the beards of prickles with which the annuli are armed, and which the animal can either shut up close to its body or let out to lay hold of the roughness of the surface upon which it creeps, and the power arising from all these of changing its place and position, affords, when compared with the provisions for motion in other animals, proofs of new and appropriate mechanism.

Suppose that we had never seen an animal move upon the ground without feet, and that the problem was to describe how such an animal might be constructed, capable of voluntarily changing place. Something, perhaps, like the organisation of reptiles *might* have been hit upon by the ingenuity of an artist, or might have been exhibited in an automaton by the combination of springs, spiral wires and ringlets. But to the solution of the problem would not be denied, surely, the praise of invention and of successful thought. Least of all could it ever be questioned whether intelligence had been employed about it or not.

Chapter Seventeen

We have already considered relation, and under different views. It was the relation of part to parts. But the bodies of animals hold in their constitution and properties a close and important relation to natures altogether external to their own – to inanimate substances and to the specific qualities of these, e.g. they hold a strict relation to the elements by which they are surrounded.

Can it doubted whether the wings of birds bear a relation to air, and the fins of fish to water? They are instruments of motion severally suited to the properties of the medium in which the motion is to be performed, which properties are different. Was not this difference contemplated when the instruments were differently constituted?

The structure of the ear depends for its use not simply on being surrounded by a fluid [i.e. air], but upon the specific nature of that fluid. Every fluid would not serve. Its particles must repel one another. It must form an elastic medium, for it is by the successive pulses of such a medium that the undulations excited by the surrounding body are carried to the organ, [so] that a communication is formed between the object and the sense – which must be done before the internal machinery of the ear, subtle as it is, can act at all.

The organs of voice and respiration are, no less than the ear, indebted for the success of their operation to the peculiar qualities of the fluid in which the animal [lives]. They therefore are constituted upon the supposition of such a fluid being always present. Change the properties of the fluid, and the organ cannot act. The structure, therefore, of the organs and the properties of our atmosphere are made for one another. Nor does it alter the relation whether you allege the organ to be made for the element (which seems the most natural way of considering it), or the element as prepared for the organ.

But there is another fluid with which we have to do, with properties of its own, [and] with laws of acting and of being acted upon, [which are] totally different from those of air and water – and that is light! To this new, this singular element, an organ is adapted, an instrument correctly adjusted, [which is] not less peculiar amongst the parts of the body than the element to which it relates. If this does not prove appropriation, I desire to know what *would* prove it! Yet the element of light and the organ of vision, however related in their office and use, have no connexion whatever in their original. The action of rays of light upon the surfaces of animals, has no tendency to breed eyes in their heads! The sun might shine forever upon living bodies without the smallest approach towards producing the sense of sight.

Throughout the universe, there is a wonderful proportioning of one thing to another. The size of animals, of the human animal especially, when considered with respect to other animals or to the plants which grow around him, is such as a regard to his conveniency would have pointed out. A giant or a pygmy could not have milked goats, reaped corn or mowed grass. We may add, could not have rode a horse, trained a vine, shorn a sheep, with the same bodily ease as we do, if at all. It may be mentioned, likewise, that the model and the materials of the human body being what they are, a much greater bulk would have broken down by its own weight. The persons of men who much exceed the ordinary stature betray this tendency!

Again (and which includes a vast variety of particulars, and those of the greatest importance), how close is the suitableness of the earth and sea to their several inhabitants, and of these inhabitants, to the place of their appointed residence! Take the earth as it is, and consider the correspondency of the powers of its inhabitants with the properties and condition of the soil which they tread. Take the inhabitants as they are, and consider the substances which the earth yields for their use. They can scratch its surface, and the surface supplies all which they want. This is the length of their faculties, and such is the constitution of the globe, and their own, that this is sufficient for all their occasions.

When we pass from the earth to the sea, from land to water, we pass through a great change. But an adequate change accompanies us of animal forms and functions, of capacities and wants, so that correspondency remains. The earth, in its nature, is very different from the sea, and the sea from the earth. But one accords with its inhabitants as exactly as the other.

The last relation of this kind which I shall mention, is that of sleep to night. And it appears to me to be a relation which was expressly intended. Two points are manifest. First, that the animal frame requires sleep. Secondly, that night brings with it a silence and a cessation of activity, which allows of sleep being taken without interruption and without loss. Animal existence is made up of action and slumber, [and] nature has provided a season for each. In the human species, for instance, were the bustle, the labour [and] the motion of life upheld by the constant presence of light, sleep could not be enjoyed without being disturbed by noise. It is happy, therefore, for this part of the creation and [the] wants of their constitution that nature, by the very disposition of her elements, has commanded, as it were, a general intermission of their toils and pursuits.

But it is not for man, either solely or principally, that night is made. Inferior natures taste its solace and expect its return with greater exactness and advantage than he does. I have often observed, and never observed but to admire, the satisfaction, no less than the regularity, with which the greatest part of the irrational world yield to this soft necessity, this grateful vicissitude. How comfortably the birds of the air, for example, address themselves to the repose of the evening – [and] with what alertness they resume the activity of the day!

Nor does it disturb our argument to confess that certain species of animal are in motion during the night and at rest in the day. With respect even to them, it is still true that there is a

155

change of condition in the animal, and an external change corresponding with it. There is still the relation, though inverted. The fact is, that the repose of other animals sets these at liberty, and invites them to their food or their sport.

If the relation of sleep to night, and in some instances its converse, be real, we cannot reflect without amazement upon the extent to which it carries us. Day and night are things close to us. The change applies immediately to our sensations. Of all the phenomena of nature, it is the most obvious and the most familiar to our experience. But, in its cause, it belongs to the great motions which are passing in the heavens. Whilst the earth glides round her axle, she ministers to the alternate necessities of the animals dwelling upon her surface, at the same time that she obeys the influence of those attractions which regulate the order of many thousand worlds. The relation, therefore, of sleep to night, is the relation of the inhabitants of the earth to the rotation of their globe. Probably it is more. It is a relation to that system of which the globe is a part, and, still further, to the congregation of systems of which theirs is only one. If this account be true, it connects the meanest individual with the universe itself – a chicken roosting upon its perch with the spheres revolving in the firmament!

But if anyone object to our representation, that the succession of day and night, or the rotation of the earth upon which it depends, is not resolvable into central attraction, we will refer him to that which certainly is – to the change of the seasons. Now, the constitution of animals susceptible of torpor, bears a relation to winter similar to that which sleep bears to night. Against not only the cold, but the want of food which the approach of winter induces, the Preserver of the world has provided in many animals, by migration, [and] in many others by torpor. As one example out of a thousand, the bat, if it did not sleep through the winter, must have starved, as the moths and flying insects upon which it feeds, disappear. But the transition from summer to winter carries us into the very midst of physical astronomy. That is to say, into the midst of those laws which govern the solar system at least, and probably all the heavenly bodies.

Chapter Eighteen

The order may not be very obvious by which I place instincts next to relations, but I consider them as a species of relation. An instinct is a propensity prior to experience, and independent of instruction. We contend that it is by instinct that the sexes seek each other, that animals cherish their offspring, that the young is directed to the teat, that birds build their nests and brood with much patience upon their eggs, that insects which do sit upon their eggs deposit them in those situations in which the young, when hatched, find their appropriate food, [and] that it is instinct which carries the salmon and some other fish out of the sea into rivers for the purpose of shedding their spawn in fresh water.

We may select out of this catalogue the incubation of eggs. I entertain no doubt but that a couple of sparrows hatched in an oven and kept separate from the rest of their species, would proceed as other sparrows do in every office which related to the production and preservation of their brood. Assuming this fact, the thing is inexplicable upon any other hypothesis than that of instinct, impressed upon the constitution of the animal. For what should induce the female bird to prepare a nest *before* she lays her eggs? It is vain to suppose her to be possessed of the faculty of reasoning, for no reasoning will reach the case. The fulness or distension which she might feel in a particular part of her body from the growth and solidity of the egg within her, could not possibly inform her that she was about to produce something which, when produced, was to be preserved and taken care of. Prior to experience, there was

157

nothing to lead to this inference or to this suspicion. The analogy was *all* against it, for, in every other instance, what issued from the body was cast out and rejected.

But secondly, let us suppose the eggs to be produced into day. How should birds know that their eggs contain their young? There is nothing, either in the aspect or in the internal composition of an egg, which could lead even the most daring imagination to conjecture that it was hereafter to turn out from under its shell a living, perfect bird. The form of the egg bears not the rudiments of a resemblance to that of the bird. Inspecting its contents, we find still less reason, if possible, to look for the result which actually takes place. If we should go so far as to guess that it might be designed for the abode and nutriment of an animal (which would be a very bold hypothesis), we should expect a tadpole dabbling in the slime rather than a dry, winged, feathered creature – a compound of parts and properties bearing no conceivable relation, either in quality or material, to anything observed in it! From the white of an egg, would anyone look for the feather of a goldfinch?

Nor would the process of incubation lead us to suspect the event. Who, that saw red streaks shooting in the fine membrane which divides the white from the yolk, would suppose that these were about to become bones and limbs? Who, that espied two discoloured points first making their appearance in the cicatrix, would have had the courage to predict that these points were to grow into the heart and head of a bird? It is difficult to strip the mind of its experience. It is difficult to resuscitate surprise when familiarity has once laid the sentiment to sleep. But could we forget all that we know, and which our sparrows *never* knew, about oviparous generation, could we divest ourselves of every information but what we derived from reasoning upon the appearances in the objects presented to us, I am convinced that Harlequin coming out of an egg upon the stage is not more astonishing to a child than the hatching of a chicken ought to be to a philosopher!

But admit the sparrow, by some means, to know that within that egg was concealed the principle of a future bird. From what chemist was she to learn that *warmth* was necessary to bring it to maturity, or that the degree of warmth imparted by the temperature of her own body was the degree required?

To suppose, therefore, that the female bird acts in this process from a sagacity and reason of her own, is to suppose her to arrive at conclusions which there are no premises to justify. If our sparrow, sitting upon her eggs, [should] expect young sparrows to come out of them, she forms, I will venture to say, a wild and extravagant expectation in opposition to present appearances and probability! She must have penetrated into the order of nature further than any faculties of ours will carry us. And it hath been well observed that this deep sagacity, if it be sagacity, subsists in conjunction with stupidity even in relation to the same subject. 'A chemical operation,' says Addison, 'could not be followed with greater art or diligence than is seen in hatching a chicken. Yet is the process carried on without the least glimmering of thought or common sense. The hen will mistake a piece of chalk for an egg, is insensible of the increase or dimunition of their number, does not distinguish between her own and those of another species, [and] is frightened when her supposititious breed of ducklings take the water.'

But it will be said that what reason could not do for the bird, observation, or instruction, or tradition might. Now if it be true that a couple of sparrows brought up in a state of separation from all other birds, would build their nest and brood upon their eggs, then there is an end to this solution. What can be the traditionary knowledge of a chicken hatched in an oven?

Of young birds taken in their nests, a few species breed when kept in cages. And they which do so, build their nests in the same manner as in the wild state, and sit upon their eggs. This is sufficient to prove an instinct without having recourse to experiments upon birds hatched by artificial heat, and deprived from their birth of all communication with their species. For we can hardly bring ourselves to believe that the parent bird informed her unfledged pupil of the history of her gestation, her timely preparation of a nest, her exclusion of the eggs, her long incubation, and of the joyful eruption at last of her expected offspring. All which the bird in her cage must have learned in her infancy if we resolve her conduct into institution.

Unless we will rather suppose that she remembers her own escape from the egg, had attentively observed the conformation of the nest in which she was nurtured, and had treasured up her remarks for future imitation. Which is not only extremely improbable (for who that sees a brood of birds in their nest can believe that they are taking a plan of their habitation?), but leaves unaccounted for one principal part of the difficulty – the preparation of the nest *before* the laying of the egg! This she could *not* gain from observation in her infancy!

It is remarkable also that the hen sits upon eggs which she has laid without any communication with the male, and which are therefore necessarily unfruitful. That secret she is not let into. Yet if the incubation had been a matter of instruction or tradition, it should seem that this distinction would have formed part of the lesson. The instinct of nature is calculated for a state of nature, the exception here alluded to taking place chiefly, if not solely, amongst domesticated fowls in which nature is forced out of her course.

There is another case of oviparous economy which is still less likely to be the effects of education, namely that of butterflies, which deposit their eggs in cabbage, from which not the butterfly herself, but the caterpillar, draws its food. The butterfly cannot taste the cabbage. Cabbage is no food for her. Yet in the cabbage, not by chance, but studiously and effectively, she lays her eggs. There are the willow-caterpillar and the cabbage-caterpillar, but we never find upon a willow the caterpillar which eats the cabbage. Nor the converse. This choice, [it] appears to me, cannot, in the butterfly, proceed from instruction. She had no teacher in her caterpillar state. I do not see, therefore, how knowledge acquired by experience, if it were ever such, could be transmitted from one generation to another. There is no opportunity either for instruction or imitation. The parent race is gone *before* the new brood is hatched! And if it be original reasoning in the butterfly, it is profound reasoning indeed. She must remember her cater-pillar state, its tastes and habits, of which memory she shows no signs whatever. She must conclude from analogy (for here recollection cannot serve), that the little round body which drops from her abdomen will at a future period produce a living creature not like herself, but like the caterpillar she remembers herself once to have been. Under the influence of these reflections, she goes about to make provision for an order of things which she concludes will take place. And it is to be observed that all butterflies [would] argue thus, all draw this conclusion, [and] all act upon it!

But suppose the address, and the selection, and the plan which we perceive in the preparations which many irrational animals make for their young, be traced to some probable origin. Still there is left to be accounted for that which is the source and foundation of these phenomena, *parental affection*, which I contend to be inexplicable upon any other hypothesis than that of instinct. For we shall hardly, in brutes, refer their conduct towards their offspring to a sense of duty, or of decency, a care of reputation, a compliance with public manners, with public laws, or with rules of life built upon a long experience of their utility! And all attempts to account for parental affection from association, I think, fail. With what is it associated? Most immediately with the throes of parturition – with pain, terror and disease!

The more remote, but not less strong association, that which depends upon analogy, is all against it. Everything else which proceeds from the body is cast away and rejected. In birds, is it the egg which the hen loves? Or is it the expectation which she cherishes of a future progeny that keeps her upon her nest? What cause has she to expect delight from her progeny? Can any rational answer be given to the question, why, prior to experience, the brooding hen should look for pleasure from her chickens? It does not, I think, appear that the cuckoo ever knows her young. Yet, in her way, she is as careful in making provision for them as any other bird!

The salmon suffers no obstacle to oppose her progress up the stream of fresh rivers. And what does she do there? She

sheds a spawn which she immediately quits in order to return
to the sea. And this issue of her body she never afterwards
recognises in any shape whatever. Where shall we find a motive
for her efforts and perseverance? Shall we seek it in argument-
ation or in instinct? The violet crab of Jamaica performs
a fatiguing march of some months' continuance from the
mountains to the seaside. When she reaches the coast, she
casts her spawn into the open sea and sets out upon her return
home!

Moths and butterflies, as hath already been observed, seek
out for their eggs those precise situations and substances in
which the caterpillar will find its food. That dear caterpillar the
parent butterfly must never see. There are no experiments to
prove that she would retain any knowledge of it if she did.
How shall we account for her conduct? I do not mean for her
art and judgment in selecting and securing a maintenance for
her young, but for the impulse upon which she acts. What
should induce her to exert any art, or judgment, or choice
about the matter? The undisclosed grub which she is destined
not to know, can hardly be the object of a particular affection
if we deny the influence of instinct. There is nothing, therefore,
left to her but that of which her nature seems incapable, an
abstract anxiety for the general preservation of the species – a
kind of patriotism, a solicitude lest the butterfly race should
cease from the creation.

Lastly, the principle of association will not explain the
discontinuance of the affection when the young animal is
grown up. Association, operating in its usual way, would
rather produce a contrary effect. Birds and beasts, after a
certain time, banish their offspring, disown their acquaintance,
seem to have even no knowledge of the objects which so lately
engrossed the attention of their minds, and occupied the
labour of their bodies. This change in different animals takes
place at different distances of time from the birth. But the time
always corresponds with the ability of the young animal to
maintain itself. [It] never anticipates it. In the sparrow tribe,
when it is perceived that the young brood can fly and shift for
themselves, then the parents forsake them forever. And though

they continue to live together, pay them no more attention than they do to other birds in the same flock. I believe the same thing is true of gregarious quadrupeds. What does all this prove but that prospection, which must be somewhere, is not in the animal, but in the Creator?

[But] neither ought it to be forgotten how much the instinct *costs* the animal which feels it. How much a bird, for example, gives up by sitting upon her nest. How repugnant it is to her habits and her pleasures. An animal formed for liberty submits to confinement in the very season when everything invites her abroad! What is more, an animal delighting in motion, made for motion, all whose motions are so easy and so free, hardly a moment at other times at rest, is, for many hours of many days together, fixed to her nest as close as if her limbs were tied down. For my part, I never see a bird in that situation but I recognise an invisible hand detaining the contented prisoner from her fields and groves, for a purpose the most worthy of sacrifice!

But loss of liberty is not the whole of what the procreant bird suffers. Harvey tells us that he has often found the female wasted to skin and bone by sitting upon her eggs.

One observation more, and I shall dismiss the subject. The pairing of birds, and the non-pairing of beasts, forms a distinction between the two classes which shows that the conjugal instinct is modified on the condition of the offspring. In quadrupeds, the young animal draws its nutriment from the body of the dam. The male parent neither does nor can contribute any part to its sustentation. In the winged race, the young bird is supplied by an importation of food, to procure and bring home which requires the industry of *both* parents. In this difference, we see a reason for the vagrant instinct of the quadruped, and for the faithful love of the feathered mate.

Chapter Nineteen

I must now crave the reader's permission to introduce into this place, for want of a better, an observation or two upon the tribe of animals belonging to land or water, which are covered by shells.

The shells of snails are a wonderful, mechanical, and if one might so speak concerning the works of nature, an original contrivance. Other animals have their proper retreats, their hybernacula also or winter-quarters, but the snail carries these about with him. He travels with his tent, and this tent, though light and thin, is completely impervious either to moisture or air. The young snail comes out of its egg with the shell upon its back, and the gradual enlargement which the shell receives is derived from the slime excreted by the animal's skin. Now the aptness of this excretion to the purpose, its property of hardening into a shell, and the action, whatever it be, of the animal whereby it avails itself of its gift, and the constitution of its glands (to say nothing of the work being commenced before the animal is born), are things which can with no probability be referred to any other cause than to express design – and that not upon the part of the animal, in which design though it might build the house, could not have supplied the material. The will of the animal could not determine the quality of the excretion. Add to which, the shell of a snail, with its pillar and convolution, is a very artificial fabric. Whilst the snail, as it should seem, is the most numb and unprovided of all artificers. In the midst of variety, there is likewise a regularity, which would hardly be expected. In the same species of snail, the number of turns is usually, if not always, the same. The sealing up of the mouth of the shell by the snail, is also well calculated for its warmth and security, but the cerate is not of the same substance with the shell.

Much of what has been observed of snails, belongs to shell-fish and their shells, particularly to those of the univalve kind, with the addition of two remarks, one of which is upon the great strength and hardness of most of these shells. I do not know whether, the weight being given, art can produce so strong a case as are some of these shells. Which defensive strength suits well with the life of an animal that has often to sustain the dangers of a stormy element and a rocky bottom, as well as the attacks of voracious fish. The other remark is upon the property in the excretion not only of congealing, but congealing in water into a cretaceous substance firm and hard. This property is much more extraordinary and, chemically speaking, more specific than that of hardening in the air, which may be reckoned like the drying of clay into bricks.

In the bi-valve order of shell-fish, cockles, mussels, oysters &c, what contrivance can be so simple or so clear as the insertion at the back of a tough, tendinous substance that becomes at once the ligament which binds the two shells together, and the hinge upon which they open and shut?

The shell of a lobster's tail, in its articulations and over-lappings, represents the jointed part of a coat of mail. Or rather, a coat of mail is an imitation of a lobster's shell. The same end is to be answered by both. The same properties, therefore, are required in both, namely hardness and flexibility [in] a covering which may guard the part without obstructing its motion. For this double purpose, the art of man expressly exercised upon the subject, has not been able to devise anything better than what nature presents to his observation. Is not this, therefore, mechanism which the mechanic, having a similar purpose in view, adopts? Is the structure of a coat of mail to be referred to art, [and] is the same structure in the lobster to be referred to anything less than art?

Some who may acknowledge the imitation, and assent to the inference which we draw from it, may be disposed to ask why such imitations are not more frequent than they are if it be true that the same principle of intelligence, design and mechanical contrivance was exerted in the formation of natural bodies as we employ in the making of various instruments by which our purposes are served? The answers to this question are, first, that it seldom happens that precisely the same purpose is pursued in any work which we compare of nature and of art. [And] secondly that it still more seldom happens that we *can* imitate nature [even] if we would! Our materials and our workmanship are equally deficient. Springs and wires, cork and leather, produce a poor substitute for an arm or a hand!

Chapter Twenty

I think a designed and studied mechanism to be, in general, more evident in animals than in plants, and it is unnecessary to dwell upon a weaker argument where a stronger is at hand. There are, however, a few observations upon the vegetable kingdom which lie so directly in our way, that it would be improper to pass by them without notice.

The one great intention in the structure of plants seems to be the perfecting of the seed, and, what is part of the same intention, the preserving of it until it be perfected. This intention shows itself by the care which appears to be taken to protect and ripen, by every advantage which can be given to them of situation in the plant, those parts which most immediately contribute to fructification, [namely] the antherae, the stamina and the stigmata. These parts are usually lodged in the centre, the recesses, or the labyrinths of the flower. During their tender and immature state, [they] are shut up in the stalk or sheltered in the bud, [and] as soon as they have acquired firmness of texture sufficient to bear exposure, and are ready to perform the office which is assigned them, they are disclosed to the light and air by the bursting of the stem or expansion of the petals. After which they have, in many cases, by the very form of the flower during its blow, the light and warmth relfected upon them from the concave side of the cup.

What is called also the *sleep* of plants, is the leaves or petals disposing themselves in such a manner as to shelter the young stems, buds or fruit. They turn up, or they fall down, according as this purpose renders either position requisite. In the growth of corn, whenever the plant begins to shoot, the two upper leaves of the stalk join together, embrace the ear and protect it till the pulp has acquired a certain degree of consistency. In some water-plants, the flowering and fecundation are carried on within the stem, which afterwards opens to let loose the impregnated seed. The pea, or papilionaceous tribe, enclose the parts of fructification within a beautiful folding of the internal blossom, sometimes called from its shape the boat or keel, itself also protected under a penthouse formed by the external petals. This structure is very artificial, and – what adds to the value of it though it may diminish the curiosity – very general.

It has also this further advantage (and it is strictly mechanical) that all the blossoms turn their *backs* to the wind whenever the gale blows strong enough to endanger the delicate parts upon which the seed depends. I have observed this a hundred times in a field of peas in blossom. It is an aptitude which results from the figure of the flower, and, as we have said, is strictly mechanical – as much so as the turning of the weather-board upon a chimney!

Of the poppy and of many similar species, the head, while it is growing, hangs down, a rigid curvature in the upper part of the stem giving to it that position. And in that position it is impenetrable by rain or moisture. When the head has acquired its size and is ready to open, the stalk erects itself for the purpose, as it should seem, of presenting the flower to the sun's rays. This always struck me as a curious property, and specifically provided for in the constitution of the plant. For, if the stem be only bent by the weight of the head, how comes it to straighten itself when the head is heaviest? These instances show the attention of nature to the principal object – the safety and maturation of the parts upon which the seed depends.

In trees, especially in those which are natives of colder climates, this point is taken up earlier. Many of these trees (observe in particular the ash and the horse-chestnut) produce the embryos of the leaves and flowers in one year, and bring them to perfection the following. There is a winter, therefore, to be gotten over. Now what we are to remark is how nature has prepared for the trials and severities of that season.

These tender embryos are in the first place wrapped up with a compactness which no art can imitate, in which state they compose what we call the bud. That is not all. The bud itself is enclosed in scales, which scales are formed from the remains of past leaves and the rudiments of future ones. Neither is this the whole. In the coldest climates a third preservative is added by the bud having a coat of gum or resin which, being congealed, resists the strongest frosts. On the approach of warm weather, this gum is softened and ceases to be a hindrance to the expansion of the leaves and flowers. All this care is part of that system of provisions which has for its object and consummation the production and perfecting of the seeds.

The seeds themselves are packed up in a capsule, a vessel composed of coats, which, compared with the rest of the flower, are strong and tough. From this vessel projects a tube, through which tube the farina, or some subtle effluvium that issues from it, is admitted to the seed. And here also occurs a mechanical variety accomodated to the different circumstances under which the same purpose is to be accomplished.

In flowers which are erect, the pistil is shorter than the stamina, and the pollen shed from the antherae into the cup of the flower, is caught in its descent by the head of the pistil called the stigma. But how is this managed when the flowers hang down (as does the crown imperial for example), and in which position the farina in its fall would be carried *from* the stigma, and not towards it? The relative strength of the parts is now inverted. The pistil in these flowers is usually longer instead of shorter than the stamina, [so] that its protruding summit may receive the pollen as it drops to the ground. In some cases (as in the nigella), where the shafts of the pistils, or stiles, are disproportionably long, they bend down their extremities upon the antherae [so] that the necessary approximation may be effected.

But (to pursue this great work in its progress), the impregnation to which all this machinery relates being completed, the other parts of the flower fade and drop off, whilst the gravid seed-vessel, on the contrary, proceeds to increase its bulk always to a great, and in some species (in the gourd, for example, and the melon) to a surprising comparative size, assuming in different plants an incalculable variety of forms, but all evidently conducing to the security of the seed.

By virtue of this process, so necessary but so diversified, we have the seed at length in stone-fruits and nuts encased in a strong shell, the shell itself enclosed in a pulp or husk by which the seed within is, or hath been, fed. Or, more generally (as in grapes, oranges and the numerous kinds of berries), plunged overhead in a glutinous syrup contained within a skin or bladder. At other times (as in apples and pears), embedded in the heart of a firm fleshy substance, or (as in strawberries) pricked into the surface of a soft pulp.

These and many more varieties exist in what we call fruits. In pulse and grain and grasses, in trees and shrubs and flowers, the variety of the seed-vessels is incomputable. We have the seeds (as in the pea tribe), regularly disposed in parchment pods which, though soft and membranous, completely exclude the wet even in the heaviest rains. The pod also, not seldom (as in the bean) lined with a fine down, [and] at other times (as in the senna) distended like a brown bladder. Or we have the seed enveloped in wool (as in the cotton plant). Lodged (as in pines) between the hard and compact scales of a cone. Or barricaded (as in the artichoke and thistle) with spikes and prickles. In mushrooms placed under a penthouse. In ferns within slits in the back part of the leaf. Or (which is the most general organisation of all) we find them covered by strong close tunicles and attached to the stem according to an order appropriated to each plant, as is seen in the several kinds of grains and grasses.

In which enumeration, what we have first to notice is unity of purpose under variety of expedients. Nothing can be more single than the design, [or] more diversified than the means. Pellicles, shells, pulps, pods, husks, skin, scales armed with thorns, are all employed in prosecuting the same intention. Secondly, we may observe that in all these cases the purpose is fulfilled within a just and limited degree. We can perceive that if the seeds of plants were more strongly guarded than they are, their greater security would interfere with other uses. Many species of animal would suffer and many perish if they could not obtain access to them. The plant would overrun the soil, or the seed be wasted for want of room to sow itself. It is, sometimes, as necessary to destroy particular species of plants as it is at other times to encourage their growth. Here, as in many cases, a balance is to be maintained between opposite uses. The provisions for the preservation of seeds appear to be directed chiefly against the inconstancy of the elements, or the sweeping destruction of inclement seasons. The depredation of animals, and the injuries of accidental violence, are allowed for in the abundance of the increase.

When nature has perfected her seeds, her next care is to disperse them. The seed cannot answer its purpose while it remains confined in the capsule. After the seeds therefore are ripened, the pericarpium opens to let them out, and the opening is not like an accidental bursting, but for the most part is according to a certain rule in each plant. What I have always thought very extraordinary, nuts and shells which we can hardly crack with our teeth, divide and make way for the little tender sprout which proceeds from the kernel. Handling the nut, I could hardly conceive how the plantule was ever to get out of it! There are cases, it is said, in which the seed-vessel, by an elastic jerk at the moment of its explosion, casts the seeds to a distance. We all, however, know that many seeds (those of most composite flowers, as of the thistle, dandelion &c) are endowed with what are not improperly called wings, that is downy appendages by which they are enabled to float in the air, and are carried oftentimes by the wind to great distances from the plant which produces them. It is the swelling also of this downy tuft within the seed-vessel that seems to overcome the resistance of its coats, and to open a passage for the seed to escape.

But the constitution of seeds is still more admirable than either their preservation or their dispersion. In the body of the seed of every species of plant, or nearly of every one, provision is made for two grand purposes, first for the safety of the germ,

[and] secondly for the temporary support of the future plant. The sprout, as folded up in the seed, is delicate and brittle beyond any other substance. It cannot be touched without being broken. Yet in beans, peas, grass-seeds, grain [and] fruits, it is so fenced on all sides, so shut up and protected, that whilst the seed itself is rudely handled, tossed into sacks [or] shovelled into heaps, the miniature plant remains unhurt. It is wonderful also how long many kinds of seeds stand out against decay. A grain of mustard-seed has been known to lie in the earth for a hundred years, and as soon as it had acquired a favourable situation, to shoot as vigorously as if just gathered from the plant!

Then, as to the second point, the temporary support of the future plant, the matter stands thus. In grain and pulse, and kernels and pippins, the germ composes a very small part of the seed. The rest consists of a nutritious substance from which the sprout draws its aliment for some considerable time after it is put forth, [namely] until the fibres shot out from the other end of the seed, are able to imbibe juices from the earth in a sufficient quantity for its demand. It is owing to this constitution that we see seeds sprout, and the sprouts make considerable progress, without any earth at all. It is an economy also in which we remark a close analogy between the seeds of plants and the eggs of animals. The same point is provided for in the same manner, in both.

In the egg, the cicatrix forms a very minute part of the contents. The white, and the white only, is expended in the formation of the chicken. The yolk, very little altered or diminished, is wrapped up in the abdomen of the young bird when it quits the shell, and serves for its nourishment till it have learnt to pick its own food. This perfectly resembles the first nutrition of a plant. In the plant, as well as in the animal, the structure has every character of contrivance belonging to it. In both, it breaks the transition from prepared to unprepared aliment. In both, it is prospective and compensatory. In animals which suck, this intermediate nourishment is supplied by a different source.

Chapter Twenty One

When we come to the elements, we take leave of our mechanics, because we come to those things of which we are confessedly ignorant. This ignorance is implied by their name. To say the truth, our investigations are stopped long before we arrive at this point. But then it is for our comfort to find that a knowledge of the constitution of the elements is not necessary for us. As Addison has well observed, 'We know water sufficiently when we know how to boil, how to freeze, how to evaporate, how to make it fresh, how to make it run or spout in what quantity and direction we please, without knowing *what* water is.'

The observation of this excellent writer has more propriety in it now than it had at the time it was made, for the constitution and the constituent parts of water appear in some measure to have been lately discovered. Yet it does not, I think, appear that we can make any better or greater use of water *since* the discovery than we did before it!

We can never think of the elements without reflecting upon the number of distinct uses which are consolidated in the same substance. The air supplies the lungs, supports fire, conveys sound, reflects light, diffuses smells, gives rain, wafts ships, [and] bears up birds. Water, besides maintaining its own inhabitants, is the universal nourisher of plants, and through them of terrestrial animals, is the basis of their juices and fluids, dilutes their food, quenches their thirst, floats their burdens. Fire warms, dissolves, enlightens, [and] is the great promoter of vegetation and life!

175

We might enlarge to almost any length we pleased upon each of these uses. But it appears to me almost sufficient to state them. The few remarks which I judge it necessary to add are as follow:

Air is essentially different from earth. There appears to be no necessity for an atmosphere's investing our globe, yet it does invest it. And we see how many, how various, and how important are the purposes which it answers to every order of animated beings which are placed upon the terrestrial surface. I think that every one of these uses will be understood upon the first mention of them, except it be that of reflecting light, which may be explained thus. If I had the power of seeing only by means of rays coming directly from the sun, whenever I turned my back upon the luminary I should find myself in darkness. If I had the power of seeing by reflected light, yet by means only of light reflected from solid masses, these masses would shine indeed, and glisten, but it would be in the dark. The hemisphere, the sky, the world could only be illuminated as it is by the light of the sun being from all sides and in every direction reflected by particles as numerous and as widely diffused as are those of the air.

Another general quality of the atmosphere is the power of evaporating fluids. The adjustment of this quality to our use is seen in its action upon the sea. In the sea, water and salt are mixed together most intimately. Yet the atmosphere raises the water and leaves the salt.

Pure and fresh drops of rain descend [which] are collected from brine. If evaporation be solution (which seems to be probable), then the air dissolves the water and not the salt. Upon whatever it be founded, the distinction is critical, so much so that when we attempt to imitate the process by art, we must regulate our distillation with great care and nicety, or together with the water we get the bitterness of the marine substance. And, after all, it is owing to this original elective power in the air that we can effect the separation which we wish by any means whatever.

By evaporation water is carried up into the air. By the converse of evaporation, it falls down upon the earth. And how does it fall? Not by the clouds being all at once reconverted into water and descending like a sheet. Not in rushing down in columns from a spout. But in moderate drops, as from a colander. Our watering-pots are made to imitate showers of rain. Yet I should have thought either of the two former methods more likely to have taken place than the last!

By respiration, flame, putrefaction, air is rendered unfit for the support of animal life. By the constant operation of these corrupting principles, the whole atmosphere, if there were no restoring causes, would come at length to be deprived of its necessary degree of purity. Some of these causes seem to have been discovered, and their efficacy ascertained by experiment. And so far as the discovery has proceeded, it opens to us a beautiful and a wonderful economy. Vegetation proves to be one of them. A sprig of mint corked up with a small portion of foul air [and] placed in the light, renders it again capable of supporting life or flame! Here, therefore, is a constant circulation of benefits maintained between the two great provinces of nature. The plant purifies what the animal has poisoned. In return, the contaminated air is more than ordinarily nutritious to the plant.

Agitation with water turns out to be another of these restoratives. The foulest air, shaken in a bottle with water for a sufficient length of time, recovers a great degree of its purity. Here then again, allowing for the scale upon which nature works, we see the salutary effects of storms and tempests. The yesty waves which confound the heaven and the sea, are doing the very thing which was done in the bottle! Nothing can be of greater importance to the living creation than the salubrity of their atmosphere. It ought to reconcile us, therefore, to these agitations of the elements of which we sometimes deplore the consequences, to know that they tend powerfully to restore to the air that purity which so many causes are constantly impairing.

In water, what ought not a little to be admired are those qualities which constitute its purity. Having no taste, it becomes the vehicle of every other. Had there been a taste in

177

water, be it what it might, it would have infected everything we ate or drank, with an importunate repetition of the same flavour. Another thing in this element not less to be admired is the constant round which it travels. And by which, without suffering either adulteration or waste, it is continually offering itself to the wants of the inhabitants of the globe. From the sea are exhaled those vapours which form the clouds. These clouds descend in showers which, penetrating into the crevices of the hills, supply springs. Which springs flow in little streams into the valleys, and there uniting become rivers. Which rivers, in turn, feed the ocean. So there is an incessant circulation of the same fluid, and not one drop, probably, more or less now than there was at the creation! Some have thought that we have too much water upon the globe, the sea occupying above three-quarters of its surface. But the expanse of ocean, immense as it is, may be no more than sufficient to fertilise the earth.

Of light it is altogether superfluous to expatiate upon the use. No man disputes it. The observations, therefore, which I shall offer, respect that little which we seem to know of its constitution.

Light travels from the sun at the rate of twelve millions of miles in a minute. Urged by such a velocity, with what force must its particles drive against every substance which stands in its way! It might seem to be a force sufficient to shatter to atoms the hardest bodies. How then is this effect, the consequence of such prodigious velocity, guarded against? By a proportionable minuteness of the particles of which light is composed. It is impossible for the human mind to imagine anything so small as a particle of light. But this extreme exility, though difficult to conceive, is easy to prove. A drop of tallow expended in the wick of a farthing candle, shall send forth rays sufficient to fill a hemisphere of a mile diameter. And to fill it so full of these rays that an aperture not larger than the pupil of an eye, wherever it be placed in the hemisphere, shall be sure to receive some of them. What floods of light are continually poured from the sun we cannot estimate. But the immensity of the sphere we can in some sort compute. The spissitude of the sun's rays at the earth is such that the number which falls upon a burning-glass of an inch diameter, is sufficient when concentrated to set wood on fire. The tenuity and the velocity of particles of light, as ascertained by separate observations, may be said to be proportioned to each other – surpassing our utmost stretch of comprehension, but proportioned! And it is this proportion alone which converts a tremendous element into a welcome visitor.

It has been observed to me by a learned friend as having often struck his mind that if light had been made by a *common* artist, it would have been of one uniform colour. Whereas, by its present composition, we have that variety of colours which is of such infinite use to us for the distinguishing of objects, which adds so much beauty to the earth and augments the stock of our innocent pleasures. With which may be joined another relfection, that considering light as of seven different colours (of which there can be no doubt, because it can be resolved into these by simply passing it through a prism), the constituent parts must be well mixed and blended together to produce a fluid so clear and colourless as a beam of light is when received from the sun.

Chapter Twenty Two

Contrivance, if established, appears to me to prove everything which we wish to prove. Amongst other things, it proves the personality of the Deity as distinguished from what is sometimes called 'nature', sometimes a 'principle' – which terms, in the mouths of those who use them philosophically, seem intended to admit an efficacy, but deny a personal agent. Now that which can contrive, which can design, must be a person. These capacities constitute personality, for they imply consciousness and thought. They require that which can perceive an end or purpose, as well as the power of providing means and of directing them to their end. They require a centre in which perceptions unite and from which volitions flow, which is mind. The acts of a mind prove the existence of a mind, and in whatever a mind resides is a person.

We have no authority to limit the properties of mind to any particular corporeal form, or to any particular circumscription of space. These properties subsist in created nature under a great variety of sensible forms. Every animated being has a certain portion of space within which perception and volition are exerted. This sphere may be enlarged to an indefinite extent – may comprehend the universe! – and being so imagined may serve to furnish us with as good a notion as we are capable of forming of the *immensity* of the Divine Nature, i.e. of a Being infinite as well in essence as in power, yet nevertheless a person.

'No man hath seen God at any time' – and this, I believe, makes the great difficulty. It is a difficulty which chiefly arises from our not duly estimating the state of our faculties. The Deity, it is true, is the object of none of our senses. But reflect what limited capacities animal senses are. Many animals seem to have but one sense, or perhaps two at the most – touch and taste. Ought such an animal to conclude against the existence of odours, sounds and colours? To another species is given the sense of smell. This is an advance in the knowledge of the powers and properties of nature. But if this favoured animal should infer from its superiority over the class last described, that it perceived everything which was perceptible in nature, it is known to us, though not suspected by the animal itself, that it proceeded upon a false and presumptuous estimate of its faculties.

To another is added the sense of hearing, which lets in a class of sensations entirely unconceived by the animal before spoken of, not only distinct but remote from any which it had ever experienced – and greatly superior to them! Yet this last animal has no more ground for believing that its senses comprehend all things which exist than might have been claimed by the tribes of animals beneath it. For we know that it is still possible to possess another sense, that of sight, which shall disclose to the percipient a new world. This fifth sense makes the animal what the *human* animal is. But to infer that possibility stops here, that either this fifth sense is the last sense or that the five comprehend all existence, is just as unwarrantable a conclusion as that which might have been made by any of the different species which possessed fewer, or even by that which possessed only one. The conclusion of the one-sense animal, and the conclusion of the five-sense animal, stand upon the same authority. There may be more and other senses than those which we have. There may be senses suited to the perception of the powers, properties and substance of higher orders of rational agents, for there is not the smallest reason for supposing that we are the highest, or that the scale of creation stops with us.

The great energies of nature are known to us only by their effects. The substances which produce them are as much concealed from our senses as the Divine essence itself.

Gravitation, though constantly present, though constantly exerting its influence, though everywhere around us, near us and within us, though diffused throughout all space and penetrating all bodies with which we are acquainted, is no object of sense to us. Is it then to be wondered at that it should in some measure be the same with the Divine nature?

Of this, however, we *are* certain, that whatever the Deity be, neither the universe nor any part of it which we see, can be He. The universe itself is merely a collective name. Its parts are all which are real, or which are things. But whatever includes marks of contrivance, whatever testifies design, necessarily carries us to Something beyond itself, to some other Being – to a Designer! No animal can have contrived its own limbs and senses, [or] can have been the author to itself of the design with which they were constructed. That supposition involves all the absurdity of self-creation, i.e. of acting without existing. Which consideration contains the answer to a question that has sometimes been asked, namely why, since something or other must have existed from eternity, may not the present universe be that something? The contrivance perceived in it proves that to be impossible. Nothing contrived can, in a strict and proper sense, be eternal, forasmuch as the contriver must have existed before the contrivance.

Wherever we see marks of contrivance, we are led for its cause to an *intelligent* author. And this understanding is founded upon experience. We see intelligence constantly contriving. That is, we see intelligence constantly producing effects [which are] marked and distinguished by certain proper-ties – not certain particular properties, but by a kind and class of properties such as relation to an end, relation of parts to one another, and to a common purpose. Furnished with this experience, we view the productions of nature. We observe them also [to be] marked and distinguished in the same manner. We wish to account for their origin, [and] our experience suggests a cause perfectly adequate to this account. No experience, no single instance or example, can be offered in favour of any other. In this cause, therefore, we ought to rest. In this cause, the common-sense of mankind has in fact rested, because it agrees with that which in all cases is the foundation of knowledge – the undeviating course of experience.

The reasoning is the same as that by which we conclude any ancient appearances to have been the effects of volcanoes or inundations, namely because they resemble the effects which fire and water produce before our eyes – and because we have never known these effects to result from any other operation! And this resemblance may subsist in so many circumstances, as not to leave us under the smallest doubt in forming our opinion. Men are not deceived by this reasoning, for whenever it happens, as it sometimes does happen, that the truth comes to be known by direct information, it turns out to be what was expected. In like manner, and upon the same foundation (which is that of experience), we conclude that the works of nature proceed from intelligence and design because, in the properties of relation to a purpose, they resemble what intelligence and design are *constantly* producing, and what nothing *except* intelligence and design ever produce at all!

Of every argument which could raise a question as to the safety of this reasoning, it may be observed that if such argument be listened to, it leads to the inference not only that the present order of nature is insufficient to prove the existence of an intelligent Creator, but that no imaginable order *would* be sufficient to prove it, [and] that no contrivance, were it ever so mechanical, ever so precise, ever so clear, ever so perfectly like those which we ourselves employ, would support this conclusion! – a doctrine to which, I conceive, no sound mind can assent.

The force, however, of the reasoning, is sometimes sunk by our taking up with mere names. We have already noticed, and we must here notice again, the misapplication of the term 'law', and the mistake concerning the idea which that term expresses in physics whenever such idea is made to take the place of power, and still more of *intelligent* power, and to be assigned for the *cause* of anything or any property that exists. This is what we are secretly apt to do when we speak of organised bodies owing their production, their form, their growth, their qualities, their beauty, [or] their use to any law of nature. I say once more that it is a perversion of language to assign any law as the efficient, operative cause of anything. A law presupposes an agent, for it is the mode according to which an agent proceeds, [and] it implies a power, for it is the order according to which that power acts. Without this agent, without this power, which are both distinct from itself, the law does nothing [and] is nothing.

What has been said concerning law, holds true of mechanism. Mechanism is not itself power. Mechanism, without power, can do nothing. Let a watch be contrived and constructed ever so ingeniously, be its parts ever so many, ever so complicated, ever so finely wrought or artificially put together, it cannot *go* without a weight or spring, i.e. without a force independent of and ulterior to its mechanism. One spring, acting in one and the same manner by simply expanding itself, may be the cause of a hundred different and useful movements, e.g. may point out the hour of the day, the day of the month, the age of the moon, the position of the planets, the cycle of the years, and many other serviceable notices according as the mechanism is better or worse contrived. But in all cases, it is necessary that the spring act at the centre!

The course of our reasoning upon such a subject, would be this. By inspecting the watch, even when [the watch was] standing still, we get a proof of contrivance and of a contriving mind having been employed about it. In the form and obvious relation of its parts, we see enough to convince us of this. If we pull the works in pieces for closer examination, we are still more fully convinced. But when we see the watch *going*, we see proof of another point, [namely] that there is a power somewhere and somehow or other applied to it, [and] that there is more in the subject that the mere wheels of the machine – in a word, that there is force and energy as well as mechanism.

So then, the watch in motion establishes to the observer two conclusions. One, that thought, contrivance and design have been employed in the forming, proportioning and arranging of its parts, and that wherever [now] he be, such a contriver there is, or was. The other, that force or power, distinct from the mechanism, is at this present time acting upon it. If I saw a hand-mill even at rest, I should see contrivance. But if I saw it grinding, I should be assured that a hand was at the windlass though in another room. It is the same in nature. In the works of nature, we trace mechanism, and this alone proves contrivance. But living, active, moving, productive nature, proves also the exertion of a power at the centre! But there must [also] be intelligence somewhere. There must be more in nature than what we see, and amongst the things unseen there must be an intelligent designing Author. The philosopher beholds with astonishment the production of things around him. Unconscious particles of matter take their stations and severally range themselves into an order so as to become collectively plants or animals, i.e. organised bodies with parts bearing strict and evident relation to one another and to the utility of the whole. And it should seem that these particles could not move in any other way than as they do, for they testify not the smallest sign of choice or liberty, or discretion. There may be particular intelligent beings guiding these motions in each case, or they may be the result of mechanical dispositions fixed beforehand by an intelligent appointment, and kept in action by a power at the centre. But in either case, there must be intelligence.

The minds of most men are fond of what they call a principle, and of the appearance of simplicity in accounting for phenomena. Yet this principle, this simplicity, resides merely in the name. The power in organised bodies of producing bodies like themselves, is one of these 'principles'. Give a philosopher this, and he can get on. But he does not reflect what this mode of production, this 'principle' (if such he choose to call it), requires – how much it presupposes, what an apparatus of instruments is necessary to its success, what a train it includes of operations and changes, one succeeding another, one related to another, one ministering to another, [and] all advancing by intermediate and sensible steps to their ultimate result! Yet because the whole of this complicated action is wrapped up in a single term 'generation', we are to set it down as an elementary principle, and to suppose that when we have resolved the things which we see into this principle, we have sufficiently accounted for their origin without the necessity of a designing, intelligent Creator.

The truth is, generation is not a principle, but a *process*! We might as well call the casting of metals a 'principle'. We might, so far as appears to me, as well call spinning and weaving 'principles', and then – referring the texture of cloths, the fabric of muslins and calicoes, the patterns of diapers and damasks to these as principles – pretend to dispense with intention, thought and contrivance on the part of the artist, or dispense indeed with the necessity of any artist at all, either in the manufacturing of the article or in the fabrication of the machinery by which the manufacture was carried on!

And, after all, how or in what sense is it true that animals produce their like? A butterfly with a proboscis instead of a mouth, four wings and six legs, produces a hairy caterpillar with jaws and teeth and fourteen feet! A frog produces a tadpole. A black beetle produces a white, smooth, soft worm. A fly a maggot! These, by a progress through different stages of life and action (in each state provided with implements and organs appropriate to the temporary nature which they bear), arrive at last at the form and fashion of the parent. But all this is process, not principle, and proves moreover that the property of animated bodies of producing their like, belongs to them not as a primordial property, not by any blind necessity in the nature of things, but as the effect of economy, wisdom and design!

The opinion which would consider generation as a principle, is confuted in my judgment not only by every mark of contrivance, for which it gives us no contriver, but by the further consideration that things generated possess a clear relation to things *not* generated! Can it be doubted, was it *ever* doubted, but that the lungs of animals bear a relation to the air? They act in it, and by it. They cannot act without it. Now, if generation produced the animal, it did not produce the air. Yet their properties correspond. The eye is made for light, and light for the eye. The eye would be of no use without light, and light perhaps of little [use] without eyes. Yet one is produced by generation, the other not.

If it be said that the air, the light, the elements – the world itself – is generated, I answer that I do not comprehend the proposition. If the term means anything similar to what it means when applied to plants and animals, the proposition is certainly without proof, and, I think, draws as near to absurdity as any proposition can do which does not include a contradiction in its terms. I am at a loss to conceive how the formation of the world can be compared to the generation of an animal. We know a cause (intelligence) adequate to the appearances which we wish to account for. We have this cause continually producing similar appearances. Yet, rejecting this cause, the sufficiency of which we know, and the action of which is constantly before our eyes, we are invited to resort to suppositions [which are] destitute of a single fact for their support!

Were it necessary to enquire into the *motives* of men's opinions, I mean their motives separate from their arguments, I should almost suspect that, because the proof of a Deity [may be] drawn from the constitution of nature, minds which are habitually in search of invention and originality, feel a resistless inclination to strike off into other solutions and other expositions. The truth is that many minds are not so indisposed to anything which can be offered to them as they are to the flatness of being content with common reason. And, what is most to be lamented, minds conscious of superiority are the most liable to this repugnancy! The 'suppositions' here alluded to, all agree in one character. They all endeavour to dispense with the necessity in nature of a particular, personal intelligence. That is to say, with the exertion of an intending, contriving mind in the structure and formation of the organised constitutions which the world contains. They would resolve all productions into unconscious energies, of a like kind in that respect with attraction, magnetism, electricity &c, without anything further.

In this, the old system of atheism and the new agree. And I much doubt whether the new schemes have advanced anything upon the old, or done more than change the terms of the nomenclature. For instance, I could never see the difference between the antiquated system of atoms, and Buffon's organic molecules. This philosopher, having made a planet by knocking off from the sun a piece of melted glass in consequence of the stroke of a comet, and having set it in motion by the same stroke both round its own axis and the sun, finds his next difficulty to be how to bring plants and animals upon it. In order to resolve this difficulty, we are to suppose the universe [to be] replenished with particles [that are] endowed with life, but without organisation or senses of their own – and endowed also with a tendency to marshal themselves into organised forms! The concourse of these particles, but without intelligence, will or direction (for I do not find any of these qualities ascribed to them) has produced the living forms which we now see.

Very few of the conjectures which philosophers hazard upon these subjects, have more of pretension in them than the challenging you to show the direct impossibility of the hypothesis. In the present example, there seemed to be a positive objection to the whole scheme upon the very face of it, which was that, if the case were as here presented, *new* combinations ought to be perpetually taking place. New plants and animals, or organised bodies which were neither, ought to be starting up before our eyes every day. For this, however, our philosopher has an answer. Whilst so many forms of plants and animals are already in existence, and consequently so many 'internal moulds', as he calls them, are prepared and at hand, the organic particles run into these moulds and are employed in supplying an accession of substance to them as well for their growth as for their propagation. By which means, things keep their ancient course. But, says the same philosopher, should any general loss or destruction of the present constitution of organised bodies take place, the particles, for want of 'moulds' into which they might enter, would run into different combinations, and replenish the waste with new species of organised substances!

Is there any history to countenance this notion? Is it known that any destruction has been so repaired – any desert thus re-peopled? So far as I remember, the only natural appearance mentioned by our author by way of fact whereon to build his hypothesis, is the formation of worms in the intestines of animals, which is here ascribed to the coalition of super-abundant organic particles floating about in the first passages, which have combined themselves into these simple animal forms for want of internal moulds into which they might be received. The thing referred to is rather a species of facts than a single fact. But to make it a fact at all, I apprehend that it is seldom difficult to suggest methods by which the eggs or spawn of these vermin may have obtained a passage into the cavities in which they are found! Add to this that their *constancy* to their species decides the question against our philosopher, if, in truth, any question remained upon the subject. [And] I trust I may be excused for not citing as another fact which is to confirm the hypothesis – a grave assertion of this writer – that the branches of trees upon which the stag feeds, break out again in his horns! Such 'facts' merit no discussion.

[But] lastly, these wonder-working instruments, these 'internal moulds' – what are they after all? What, when examined, but a name without signification? Unintelligible, if not self-contradictory? At best, differing in nothing from the 'essential forms' of Greek philosophy? One short sentence of Buffon's work exhibits his scheme: 'When this nutritious and prolific matter, which is diffused throughout all nature, passes through the internal mould of an animal or vegetable, and finds a proper matrix or receptacle, it gives rise to an animal or vegetable of the same species.'

Does any reader annex a meaning to the expression 'internal mould' in this sentence? Ought it then to be said that, though we have little notion of an internal mould, we have not much more of a designing mind? The very *contrary* of this assertion is the truth. When we speak of an artificer or an architect, we talk of what is comprehensible to our understanding and familiar to our experience. We use no other terms than what refer us for their meaning to our consciousness and observation. Whereas names like that [which] we have mentioned, refer us to nothing – excite no idea! [They] convey a sound, but, I think, do no more.

Another system which has lately been brought forward, and with much ingenuity, is that of appetencies. The short account of the theory is this: Pieces of soft ductile matter being endued with propensities, or appetencies, for particular actions, would, by continual endeavours carried on through a long series of generations, work themselves gradually into suitable forms, and at length acquire by imperceptible improvements an organisation fitted to the action which their propensities led them to exert. A piece of animated matter, for example, that was endued with a propensity to fly, though ever so shapeless, though no other than a round ball, would, in a course of ages if not in a million years, perhaps in a hundred millions of years (for our theorists having eternity to dispose of, are never sparing in time), acquire wings! The same tendency to loco-motion in an aquatic animal, or rather in an animated lump which might happen to be surrounded by water, would end in the production of fins. A living substance confined to the earth would put out legs and feet, or if it took a different turn would break the body into ringlets and conclude by crawling upon the ground.

Although I have introduced the mention of this theory into this place, I am unwilling to give it the name of an atheistic scheme because the original propensities are attributed to the ordination and appointment of an intelligent and designing Creator. In one important respect, however, the theory coin-cides with atheistic systems in that it does away [with] final causes. Instead of the parts of a plant or animal having been intended for the use to which we see them applied, according to this theory they have themselves grown out of that action [or] sprung from that use. The theory therefore dispenses with that which we insist upon – the necessity in each case of an intelligent designing mind for the determining of forms which organised bodies bear!

The scheme under consideration is open to the same objection with conjectures of a similar tendency – a total defect of evidence! No changes like those which the theory requires have ever been observed. All the changes in Ovid's *Metamorphoses* might have been effected by these appetencies if the theory were true. Yet not an example, nor the pretence of an example, is offered of a single change being known to have taken place. Nor is the order of generation obedient to the principle upon which this theory is built. The mammae of the male have not vanished by inusitation. It is easy to say, and it has been said, that the process is too slow to be perceived. That it has been carried on through tracts of immeasurable time, and that the present order of things is the result of a gradation of which no human record can trace the steps. It is easy to say this, and yet it is still true that the hypothesis remains destitute of evidence.

The analogies which have been alleged, are of the following kind: The bunch of a camel is said to be no other than the effect of carrying burdens, a service in which the species has been employed from the most ancient times of the world. The first race, by daily loading of the back, would find a small tumour in the flesh of that part. The next progeny would bring this tumour into the world with them. The life to which they were destined would increase it, [and] being continued it would go on through every succession to augment its size till it attained the bulk under which it now appears. This may serve for one instance. Another is taken from certain birds. The crane, the heron, the bittern [and] the stork, have their thighs bare of feathers. This is accounted for from the habit of wading in water, and from the effect of that element to check the growth of feathers upon these parts. The feathers declined through each generation, [and] the down became weak and thin till the deterioration ended in absolute nakedness. I will mention a third instance, and that is the pouch of the pelican. This extraordinary conformation is nothing more, say our philosophers, than the result of habit through a long series of generations. The pelican soon found the conveniency of reserving in its mouth, when its appetite was glutted, there-mainder of its prey, which is fish. The fulness produced by this attempt stretched the skin [and] every distension increased the cavity. The original bird, and many generations which succeeded him, might find difficulty enough in making the pouch answer this purpose. But future pelicans entering upon a life with a pouch derived from their progenitors of considerable capacity, would more readily accelerate its advance to perfection by frequently pressing down the sac with the weight of fish which it might now contain.

These, or this kind, are the analogies relied upon. Now in the first place, the instances themselves are unauthenticated by testimony, and to say the least, open to great objections. Whoever read of camels *without* bunches? A bunch not unlike the camel's is found between the shoulders of the buffalo, [for] the origin of which it is impossible to give the account here given! In the second example, why should the application of water which appears to thicken the growth of feathers upon the bodies and breasts of geese and swans and other waterfowl, have divested of this covering the thighs of cranes? The third instance, which appears to be as plausible as any that can be produced, has this against it – that it is a singularity restricted to the species. If it had its commencement in the cause and manner which have been assigned, the like conformation might be expected to take place in *other* birds which fed upon fish! How comes it to pass that the pelican alone was the inventress, and her descendants the only inheritors of this curious resource?

But it is the less necessary to controvert the instances themselves, as it is a straining of analogy beyond all limits of reason to assert that birds, beasts and fish, with all their variety and complexity of organisation, have been brought into their forms and distinguished into their several kinds and natures by the same process (even if that process could be demonstrated, or had it ever actually been noticed) as might seem to serve for the gradual generation of a camel's bunch, or a pelican's pouch. The tendency is all the other way. These parts could not grow out of their use though they had eternity to grow in!

The senses of animals appear to me altogether incapable of receiving the explanation of their origin which this theory affords. Including under the word 'sense' the organ and the perception, we have no account of either. How will our philosopher get at vision, or make an eye? How should the blind animal affect sight, of which blind animals have neither conception nor desire? Affecting it by endeavour to see, could it so determine the fluids of its body as to inchoate the formation of an eye? Or suppose the eye formed, would the perception follow? The same of the other senses. And this objection holds its force, ascribe what you will to the hand of time, to the power of habit, to changes too slow to be observed by man. Concede what you please to these arbitrary and unattested suppositions, how will they help you? Here is no inception. No laws, no course, no powers of nature which prevail at present, nor any analogous to these, would give commencement to a new sense. And it is vain to enquire how that might proceed which could never begin!

I think the senses to be the most inconsistent with the hypothesis before us of any part of the animal frame. But other parts are sufficiently so. If we could suppose joints and muscles to be gradually formed by action and exercise, what action or exercise could form a skull or fill it with brains? No effort of the animal could determine the clothing of its skin. What conatus could give prickles to the porcupine or hedgehog, or to the sheep its fleece? In the last place, what do these appetencies mean when applied to plants? I am not able to give a signification to the term which can be transferred from animals to plants, or which is common to both. Yet a no less successful organisation is found in plants than what obtains in animals. A solution is wanted for one as well as the other.

Upon the whole, after all the schemes and struggles of a reluctant philosophy, the necessary resort is to a Deity. The marks of design are too strong to be gotten over. Design *must* have had a Designer. That Designer *must* have been a Person. That Person is God.

Chapter Twenty Three

It is an immense conclusion that there is a God – a perceiving, intelligent, designing Being at the head of creation and from Whose will it proceeded. The attributes of such a Being, suppose His reality to be proved, must be adequate to the magnitude, extent and multiplicity of His operations, which are not only vast beyond comparison with those performed by any other power, but infinite, because they are unlimited on all sides. Yet the contemplation of a nature so exalted, however surely we arrive at the proof of its existence, overwhelms our faculties. One consequence of which is that from painful abstraction, the thoughts seek relief in sensible images. Whence may be deduced the ancient and almost universal propensity to idolatrous substitutions. They are the recourses of a labouring imagination. False religions usually fall in with the natural propensity. True religions, or such as have derived themselves from the true, resist it.

It is one of the advantages of the revelations which we acknowledge, that, whilst they reject idolatry with its many pernicious accompaniments, they introduce the Deity to human apprehension under an idea more personal, more determinate, more within its compass than the theology of nature can do. And this they do by representing Him exclusively under the relation in which He stands to ourselves, and for the most part under some precise character resulting from that relation or from the history of His providences. Which method suits the span of our intellects much better than the universality which enters into the idea of God from the views of nature. When, therefore, these representations are well founded in authority (for all depends upon that), they afford a condescension to the state of our faculties, of which they who have most reflected upon the subject, will be the first to acknowledge the want and the value.

Nevertheless, if we be careful to imitate the documents of our religion, by confining our explanations to what concerns ourselves, and do not affect more precision in our ideas than the subject allows of, the several terms which are employed to denote the attributes of the Deity may be made even in natural religion to bear a sense consistent with truth and reason, and not surpassing our comprehension. These terms are: Omnipotence, omniscience, omnipresence, eternity, self-existence, necessary existence, [and] spirituality.

'Omnipotence', 'omniscience', 'infinite' power, 'infinite' knowledge, are superlatives, expressing our conception of these attributes in the strongest and most elevated terms which language supplies. We ascribe power to the Deity under the name of 'omnipotence', the strict and correct conclusion being that power which could create such a world as this is, must be beyond all comparison greater than any which we experience in ourselves, than any which we observe in other visible agents, greater also than any which we can want for our individual protection and preservation in the Being upon whom we depend. It is a power, likewise, to which we are not authorised by our observation or knowledge to assign any limits of space or duration.

Very much of the same is applicable to 'omniscience' – infinite knowledge, or infinite wisdom. In strictness of language, there is a difference between knowledge and wisdom, wisdom always supposing action, and action directed by it. With respect to knowledge, the Creator must know intimately the constitution and properties of the things which He created. Which seems also to imply a foreknowledge of their action upon one another, and of their changes, at least so far as the same [changes] result from trains of physical and necessary causes. His omniscience also, as far as respects things present, is deducible from His nature as an intelligent Being, joined with the extent or universality of His operations. Where He acts, He is. And where He is, He perceives.

The wisdom of the Deity, as testified in the works of creation, surpasses all idea we have of wisdom drawn from the highest class of intelligent beings with whom we are acquainted. And, what is of the chief importance to us, whatever be its compass or extent, which it is evidently impossible that we should determine, it must be adequate to the conduct of that order of things under which we live. And this is enough. It is of very inferior consequence by what terms we express our notion, or rather our admiration, of this attribute. The terms which the piety and the usage of language have rendered habitual to us, may be as proper as any other. We can trace this attribute much beyond what is necessary for any conclusion to which we have occasion to apply it. The degree of knowledge and power requisite for the formation of created nature, cannot, with respect to us, be distinguished from infinite.

The Divine omnipresence stands in natural theology upon this foundation – in every part and place of the universe with which we are acquainted, we perceive the exertion of a power which we believe to proceed from the Deity. In what part or point of space that has ever been explored, do we not discover attraction? In what regions do we not find light? In what accessible portion of our globe do we not meet with gravity, magnetism [and] electricity, together with organised vegetable or animal nature? Nay, further we may ask, what kingdom is there of nature, what corner of space, in which there is anything that can be examined by us, where we do not fall upon contrivance and design? The only reflection, perhaps, which arises in our minds from this view of the world around us, is that the laws of nature everywhere prevail – that they are uniform and universal. But what do we mean by the laws of nature, or *any* law?

Effects are produced by power, not by laws. A law cannot execute itself. A law refers us to an agent. Now an agency so general that we cannot discover its absence, may be called universal, and the person or Being in Whom that power resides may be taken to be omnipresent. He who upholds all things by His power, may be said to be everywhere present. This is called a *virtual* presence. There is also what metaphysicians denominate an essential ubiquity, which idea the language of Scripture seems to favour. But the former, I think, goes as far as natural theology carries us.

'Eternity' is a negative idea clothed with a positive name. It supposes a *present* existence, and is the negation of a beginning or an end of that existence. As applied to the Deity, there never was a time in which *nothing* [not even God] existed, because that condition *must* have continued. Nothing could rise up out of it. Nothing could ever have existed since, [and] nothing could exist now. In strictness, however, we have no concern with duration prior to that of the visible world. Upon this article of [natural] theology, it is sufficient to know that the contriver necessarily existed before the contrivance.

'Self-existence' is another negative idea, [namely] the negation of a preceding cause as of a progenitor, a maker, an author, [or] a creator. 'Necessary existence' means demonstrable existence.

'Spirituality' expresses an idea made up of a negative and of a positive part. The negative part consists in the exclusion of some of the known properties of matter, especially of solidity and of gravitation. The positive part comprises perception, thought, will, power, [and] action, by which last term is meant the origination of motion, the quality, perhaps, in which resides the essential superiority of spirit over matter which cannot move unless it be moved, and cannot *but* move when impelled by another. I apprehend that there can be no difficulty in applying to the Deity both parts of this idea.

Chapter Twenty Four

Of the unity of the Deity, the proof is the uniformity of plan observable in the universe. The universe itself is a system, each part either depending upon other parts, or being connected with other parts by some common law of motion or by the presence of some common substance. One principle of gravitation causes a stone to drop towards the earth, *and* the moon to wheel around it! One law of attraction carries all the different planets about the sun. There are also other points of agreement amongst them which may be considered as marks of the identity of their origin, and of their intelligent Author.

In all are found the conveniency and stability derived from gravitation. They all experience [the] vicissitudes of days and nights and changes of season. They all, at least Jupiter, Mars and Venus, have the same advantages from their atmosphere as we have. In all the planets, the axes of rotation are permanent. Nothing is more probable than that the same attracting influence, acting according to the same rule, reaches to the fixed stars. But, if this be only probable, another thing is certain, [namely] that the same element of *light* does. The light from a fixed star affects our eyes in the same manner, is refracted and reflected according to the same laws, as the light of a candle. The velocity of the light of the fixed stars is also the same as the velocity of the light of the sun reflected from the satellites of Jupiter. The heat of the sun, in kind, differs nothing from the heat of a coal fire!

In our own globe, the case is clearer. New countries are continually discovered, but the old laws of nature are always found in them. New plants, perhaps, or animals, but always in company with plants and animals which we already know, and always possessing many of the same general properties. We never get amongst such original or totally different modes of existence as to indicate that we are come into the province of a different Creator, or under the direction of a different will. The same order of things attends us wherever we go. The elements act upon one another, electricity operates, the tides rise and fall, the magnetic needle elects its position in one region of the earth and sea as well as in another. One atmosphere invests all parts of the globe and connects all. One sun illuminates. One moon exerts its attraction on all parts. This, surely, bespeaks the same creation and the same Creator.

Chapter Twenty Five

The proof of the Divine goodness rests upon two propositions, each, we contend, capable of being made out by observations drawn from the appearances of nature.

The first is that, in a vast plurality of instances in which contrivance is perceived, the design of the contrivance is *beneficial*. The second, that the Deity has superadded *pleasure* to animal sensations beyond what was necessary for any other purpose – or when the purpose, so far as it *was* necessary, might have been effected by the operation of pain.

First, instances in which the design is beneficial:

No productions of nature display contrivance so manifestly as the parts of animals. Now, when the multitude of animals is considered, the number of parts in each, their figure and fitness, the faculties depending upon them, the variety of species, the complexity of structure, the success and felicity of the result, we can never reflect without the profoundest adoration upon the character of that Being from Whom all these things have proceeded. What an exertion of benevolence creation was – how minute its care, how vast its comprehension!

When we appeal to the parts and faculties of animals, and to the limbs and senses in particular, we state, I conceive, the proper proof for the conclusion we wish to establish. I will not say that the insensible parts of nature are made solely for the sensitive parts. But this I say, that, when we consider the benevolence of the Deity, we can only consider it in relation to sensitive being. Without this reference, the attribute has no object [and] the term has no meaning. Dead matter is nothing. The parts, therefore, especially the limbs and senses of animals, are instruments of perception. They compose what may be called the whole of visible nature estimated with a view to the disposition of its Author. Consequently, it is in these that we are to seek His character. It is by these that we are to prove that the world was made with a benevolent design.

Nor is the design abortive. It is a happy world after all. The air, the earth, the water, teem with delighted existence. In a spring noon or a summer evening, on whichever side I turn, myriads of happy beings crowd upon my view. Swarms of new-born flies are trying their pinions in the air. Their sportive motions, their wanton mazes, their gratuitous activity, their continual change of place without use or purpose, testify their joy and the exultation which they feel in their lately discovered faculties. A bee amongst the flowers in spring is one of the most cheerful objects that can be looked upon. Its life appears to be all enjoyment – so busy and so pleased! Yet it is only a species of insect life with which, by reason of the animal being half domesticated, we happen to be better acquainted than we are with others. The whole winged insect tribe, it is probable, are equally intent upon their proper employments, gratified by the offices which the Author of their nature has assigned to them.

If we look to the waters, shoals of fish frequent the margins of rivers, of lakes, and of the sea itself. These are so happy that they know not what to do with themselves. Their attitudes, their vivacity, their leaps out of the water, their frolics in it (which I have noticed a thousand times with equal attention and amusement), all conduce to show their excess of spirits, and are simply the effects of that excess. Walking by the seaside in a calm evening, and with an ebbing tide, I have frequently remarked the appearance of a dark cloud, or rather very thick mist, hanging over the edge of the water to the height, perhaps, of half a yard and of the breadth of two or three yards, stretching along the coast as far as the eye could reach, and always retiring with the water. When this cloud came to be examined, it proved to be nothing else than so much space filled with young *shrimps* in the act of bounding into the air from the water or wet sand. If any motion of a mute animal could express delight, it was this. If they had meant to make signs of their happiness, they could not have done it more intelligibly. Suppose then, what I have no doubt of, each individual of this number to be in a state of positive enjoyment – what a sum, collectively, of gratification and pleasure have we here!

The young of all animals appear to me to receive pleasure simply from the exercise of their limbs and faculties, without reference to any end to be attained or any use to be answered by the exertion. A child, without knowing anything of the use of language, is in a high degree delighted with being able to speak. Its incessant repetition of a few articulate sounds or, perhaps, of the single word which it has learned to pronounce, proves this point clearly. Nor is it less pleased with its first successful endeavours to walk, or rather to run (which precedes walking), although entirely ignorant of the import-ance of the attainment to its future life, and even without applying it to any present purpose. A child is delighted with speaking without having anything to say! And with walking, without knowing where to go! And, prior to both these, I am disposed to believe that the waking hours of infancy are agreeably taken up with the exercise of vision, or perhaps more properly speaking, with learning to see.

But it is not for youth alone that the great Parent of creation hath provided. Happiness is found with the purring cat – no less than with the playful kitten – in the armchair of dozing age or the animation of the chase. To novelty, to acuteness of sensation, to ardour of pursuit, succeeds in no inconsiderable degree [the] perception of ease. Herein is the difference between young and old. The young are not happy but when enjoying pleasure. The old are happy when free from pain. Youth was to be stimulated by impatience of rest, whilst to age quietness and repose become positive gratifications. In one important respect, the advantage is with the old. A state of ease is, generally speaking, more attainable than a state of pleasure. A constitution, therefore, which can enjoy ease, is preferable to that which can taste only pleasure.

This same perception of ease renders old age a condition of great comfort, especially after a busy or tempestuous life. It is well described by Rousseau to be the interval between the hurry and the end of life. How far the same cause extends to other animal natures cannot be judged of with certainty, [but] the appearance of satisfaction with which most animals, as their activity subsides, seek and enjoy rest affords reason to believe that this gratification is appointed to advanced life under all its various forms.

Animal enjoyments are infinitely diversified. The modes of life of different animals are not only of various, but of opposite kinds. Yet each is happy in its own. Animals of prey live much alone. Animals of a milder constitution, [live] in society. The herring which lives in shoals, and the sheep which lives in flocks, are not more happy in a crowd than is the pike or the lion with the deep solitudes of the pool or the forest.

It will be said that the instances which we have brought forward, whether of vivacity or repose, or of apparent enjoyment derived from either, are picked and favourable instances. We answer that they are instances nevertheless which comprise large provinces of existence. That very case which we have described, is the case of millions! At this moment, in *every* given moment of time, how many myriads of animals are eating their food, gratifying their appetites, ruminating in their holes, accomplishing their wishes, pursuing their pleasures [or] taking their pastimes? We contend that throughout the whole of life, looking to the sensations, the plurality and the preponderancy is in favour of happiness by a vast excess. In our own species, the prepollency of good over evil, of health and ease over pain and distress, is evinced by the very notice which calamities excite. What enquiries does the sickness of our friends produce? What conversation their misfortunes? This shows that the *common* course of things is in favour of happiness – that happiness is the rule, [and] misery the exception! Were the order reversed, our attention would be called to examples of health and competency instead of disease and want.

One great cause of our insensibility to the goodness of the Creator, is the very extensiveness of His bounty. We prize but little what we share only in common with the rest of our species. When we hear of blessings, we think forthwith of successes, of prosperous fortunes, of honours, riches, preferments, i.e. of those advantages and superiorities over others which we happen either to possess or to be in pursuit of. The *common* benefits of our nature entirely escape us. Yet these are the *great* things! These constitute what most properly ought to be accounted blessings of Providence. Nightly rest and daily bread, the ordinary use of our limbs and senses – and understandings! – are gifts which admit of no comparison with any other. Yet because almost every man we meet with possesses these, we leave them out of our enumeration. They raise no sentiment. They move no gratitude, [and] herein is our judgment perverted by our selfishness.

A blessing ought, in truth, to be the more satisfactory by its very diffusion, its commonness, its cheapness – by its falling to the lot, and forming the happiness, of the great bulk and body of our species as well as of ourselves. Nay, even when we do not possess it, it ought to be [a] matter of thankfulness that *others* do! But we have a different way of thinking. We court distinction. That is not the worst – we see nothing but what has distinction to recommend it! This necessarily contracts our views of the Creator's beneficence within a narrow compass, and most unjustly. It is in those things which are so common as to be no distinction that the amplitude of the Divine benignity is perceived!

When God created the human species, either He wished their happiness, or He wished their misery. Or He was indifferent and unconcerned about either. If He had wished our misery, He might have made sure of His purpose by forming our senses to be so many sores and pains to us as they are now instruments of gratification and enjoyment! Or by placing us amidst objects so ill suited to our perceptions as to have continually offended us, instead of ministering to our refreshment and delight. He might have made, for example, everything we saw loathsome, everything we touched a sting, every smell a stench and every sound a discord.

If He had been indifferent about our happiness or misery, we must impute to our good fortune (as all design by this supposition is excluded) both the capacity of our senses to receive pleasure and the supply of external objects fitted to produce it! But either of these being too much to attribute to accident, nothing remains but the first supposition, that God, when He created the human species, wished their happiness. Contrivance proves design, and the predominant tendency of the contrivance indicates the disposition of the designer. The world abounds with contrivances, and all the contrivances which we are acquainted with are directed to beneficial purposes. Evil, no doubt, exists, but is never, that we can perceive, the object of contrivance. Teeth are contrived to eat, not to ache. Their aching now and then is incidental to the contrivance – but it is not the object of it!

This is a distinction which well deserves to be attended to. In describing implements of husbandry, you would hardly say of the sickle that it was made to cut the reaper's hand, though from the construction of the instrument and the manner of using it, this mischief often follows. But if you had occasion to describe instruments of torture or execution, this engine you would say is to extend the sinews, this to dislocate the joints, this to break the bones, [and] this to scorch the soles of the feet! Here, pain and misery are the very objects of the contrivance. Now, nothing of *this* sort is to be found in the works of nature. We never discover a train of contrivance to bring about an evil purpose. No anatomist ever discovered a system of organisation *calculated* to produce pain and disease. Or in explaining the parts of the human body, ever said this is to irritate, this to inflame, this duct is to convey the gravel to the kidneys, this gland to secrete the humour which forms the gout! If by chance he comes at a part of which he knows not the use, the most he can say is that it is useless. No one ever suspects that it was put there to annoy or to torment.

The two cases which appear to have the most difficulty in them as forming the exception, are those of venomous animals, and of animals preying upon one another. These properties must be referred to design, because there is in all cases an express and distinct organisation provided for them. Under the first head, the fangs of vipers, the stings of wasps and scorpions, are as clearly intended for their purpose as any animal structure. And the same thing must be acknowledged of the talons and beaks of birds, of the tusks, teeth and claws of beasts of prey, of the shark's mouth, of the spider's web, and of numberless weapons of offence belonging to different insects. We cannot, therefore, avoid the difficulty by saying that the effect was not intended. The only question is whether it be evil.

From the benevolence which pervades the general designs of nature, we ought to presume that these consequences, if they could enter into our calculation, would turn the balance on the favourable side. With respect to venomous bites and stings, it may be observed that, the animal itself being regarded, the faculty complained of is good, being conducive in all cases to the defence of the animal, the subduing of its prey, [and] to the killing of it when caught by a mortal wound, which may be no less merciful to the victim than salutary to the devourer. In the viper, for instance, the poisonous fang may do that which in other animals is done by the crush of the teeth. Frogs and mice might be swallowed alive without it.

But it will be said that this provision when it comes to the case of bites, deadly even to human bodies and to those of large quadrupeds, is greatly overdone. That it might have fulfilled its use and yet have been much less deleterious than it is. Now I believe the case of bites which produce death in large animals (of stings I think there are none) to be very few. The experiments of the Abbé Fontana, which were numerous, go strongly to the proof of this point. He found that it required the action of five exasperated vipers to kill a dog of moderate size, but that to the killing of a mouse or a frog, a single bite was sufficient – which agrees with the use which we assign to the faculty. It has been [also], I think, very justly remarked concerning serpents that whilst only a few species possess the venomous property, that property guards the whole tribe. The most innocuous snake is avoided with as much care as a viper. The terror with which large animals regard this class of reptile is its protection, and this terror is founded on the formidable revenge which a few of the number, compared with the whole, are capable of taking. The species of serpents described by Linnaeus amount to two hundred and eighteen, of which thirty-two only are poisonous.

The pursuit of prey forms the employment, and appears to constitute the pleasure, of a considerable part of the animal creation. The using of the means of defence, or flight or precaution, forms also the business of another part. And even of this latter tribe, we have no reason to suppose that their happiness is much molested by their fears. Their danger exists continually, and in some cases they seem to be so far sensible of it as to provide in the best manner they can against it. But it is only when the attack is actually made upon them that they appear to suffer from it. To contemplate the insecurity of their condition with anxiety and dread requires a degree of reflection which (happily for themselves) they do not possess. A hare, notwithstanding the number of its dangers and its enemies, is as playful an animal as any other.

But to do justice to the question, the system of animal destruction ought always to be considered in strict connexion with another property of animal nature, super-fecundity. They are countervailing qualities. One subsists by the correction of the other. In almost all cases, nature produces her supplies with profusion. A single cod-fish spawns in one season a greater number of eggs that all the inhabitants of England amount to! A thousand other instances of prolific generation might be stated which, though not equal to this, would carry on the increase of the species with a rapidity which outruns calculation. But then this super-fecundity, though of occasional use and importance, exceeds the ordinary capacity of nature to receive or support its progeny. All superabundance supposes destruction, or must destroy itself, [for] if any single species were left to their natural increase without disturbance or restraint, the food of other species would be exhausted by their maintenance. It is necessary, therefore, that the effects of such prolific faculties be curtailed.

In conjunction with other checks and limits, are the thinnings which take place among animals by their action upon one another. We ourselves experience the use of these hostilities. One species of insect rids us of another species, or reduces their ranks. A third species, perhaps, keeps the second within bounds. And birds and lizards are a fence against the inordinate increase by which even these last might infest us. What further shows that the system of destruction amongst animals holds an express relation to the system of fecundity – that they are parts indeed of one compensatory scheme – is that in each species the fecundity bears a proportion to the smallness of the animal, to the weakness, to the shortness of its natural term of life, and to the dangers and enemies by which it is surrounded. An elephant produces but one calf [where] a butterfly lays six hundred eggs. Birds of prey seldom produce more than two eggs [where] the sparrow and the duck frequently sit upon a dozen. In the rivers, we meet with a thousand minnows for one pike, [and] in the sea a million herrings for one shark. Compensation obtains throughout. Defencelessness and devastation are repaired by fecundity.

Chapter Twenty Six

Natural theology has ever been pressed with the question, why, under the regency of a supreme and benevolent Will, should there be in the world so much appearance of chance? The question in its *whole* compass lies beyond our reach, but there are not wanting answers which seem to have considerable weight, and to embrace a considerable number of cases. There *must* be chance in the midst of design. By which we mean that events which are not designed, [must] necessarily arise from the pursuit of events which *are* designed. One man travelling to York meets another man travelling to London. Their meeting is by chance, is accidental, and so would be called and reckoned though the journeys which produced the meeting were both undertaken with design and deliberation. The meeting, though accidental, was hypothetically necessary (which is the only sort of necessity that is intelligible), for, if the two journeys were commenced at the time [and] in the direction and speed with which they were, in fact, begun and performed, the meeting could not be avoided. The rencontre might be most unfortunate, though the errands upon which each party set out upon his journey were the most innocent or the most laudable. [But] the by-effect may be unfavourable without impeachment of the proper purpose.

The appearance of chance will always bear a proportion to the ignorance of the observer. The cast of a dice as regularly follows the laws of motion as the going of a watch. Yet, because we can trace the operation of those laws through the works and movements of the watch, and cannot trace them in the shaking and throwing of the dice (though the laws be the same and prevail equally in both cases), we call the turning up of the number of the dice chance, [but] the pointing of the index of the watch, machinery, order, or some [other] name which excludes chance.

It is the same in those events which depend upon the will of a free and rational agent. The verdict of a jury, the sentence of a judge, the resolution of an assembly, the issue of a contested election, will have more or less the appearance of chance according as we were less or more acquainted with the reasons which influenced the deliberation. The difference resides in the information of the observer, and not in the thing itself, which in all the cases proposed, proceeds from intelligence, from mind, from counsel [and] from design.

Now, when this *one* cause of the appearance of chance, the ignorance of the observer, comes to be applied to the operations of the Deity, it is easy to foresee how fruitful it must prove of difficulties and of seeming confusion. It is only [necessary for us] to think of the Deity to perceive what variety of objects, what distance of time, what extent of space and action His counsels may, or rather *must*, comprehend! Can it be wondered at that of the purposes which dwell in such a Mind as this, so small a part should be known to us? It is only necessary, therefore, to bear in our thought that, in proportion to the inadequateness of our information, will be the quantity in the world of apparent chance.

In a great variety of cases, it appears to be better that events rise up by chance – [or] more properly with the *appearance* of chance – than according to observable rule. For example, it seems to be expedient that the period of human life should be uncertain. Did mortality follow any fixed rule, it would produce a security in those that were at a great distance from it – which would lead to the greatest disorders – and a horror in those who approached it similar to that which a condemned prisoner feels on the night before his execution. But, [so] that death [might] be uncertain, the young must sometimes die as well as the old. Were deaths never sudden, they who are in health would be too confident of life. The strong and the active

212

– who want *most* to be warned and checked – would live without apprehension or restraint. On the other hand, were sudden deaths very frequent, the sense of constant jeopardy would interfere too much with the degree of ease and enjoyment intended for us, and human life [would] be too precarious for the business and interests which belong to it. There could not be dependence either upon our own lives or the lives of those with whom we are connected, sufficient to carry on the regular offices of human society. The manner, therefore, in which death is made to occur, conduces to admonition without overthrowing the necessary stability of human affairs.

The seasons are a mixture of regularity and chance. They are regular enough to authorise expectation, whilst their being in a considerable degree irregular, induces on the part of the cultivators of the soil a necessity for personal attendance, for activity, vigilance, precaution. It is this necessity which creates farmers. Uncertainty, therefore, has its use even to those who sometimes complain of it the most!

Chapter Twenty Seven

In all cases wherein the mind feels itself in danger of being confounded by variety, it is sure to rest upon a few strong points, or perhaps upon a single instance. Amongst a multitude of proofs, it is *one* [proof] that does the business. [And] if we observe in any argument that hardly two minds fix upon the *same* instance, the diversity of choice shows the strength of the argument because it shows the number and competition of the examples.

There is no subject in which the tendency to dwell upon select or single topics is so usual as that of natural history [when] applied to the proof of an intelligent Creator. For my part, I take my stand in human anatomy and the examples of mechanism from the copious catalogue which it supplies. To these the reader's memory will go back as they are severally set forth in their places. There is not one of the number which I do not think decisive. Nor have I read or heard of any solution to these appearances which in the smallest degree shakes the conclusion that we build upon them.

Of those who, either in this book or any other, read arguments to prove the existence of God, it will be said that they leave off only where they began, and that they were never ignorant of this great truth, never doubted of it, [and] that it does not therefore appear what is gained by researches from which no new opinion is learnt and upon which no proofs were wanted. Now I answer, that by investigation the following points are *always* gained in favour of doctrines even the most generally acknowledged, [namely] stability and impression.

Occasions will arise to try the firmness of our most habitual opinions. And upon these occasions it is a matter of incalculable use to feel our foundation – to find a support in argument for what we had taken up upon authority. In the present case, the arguments upon which the conclusion rests are exactly such as a truth of universal concern *ought* to rest upon!

But what is gained by research in the stability of our conclusion, is also gained from it in impression. I take the case to be this: Perhaps almost every man living has a particular train of thought into which his mind glides and falls when at leisure, from the impressions and ideas that occasionally excite it. Perhaps also the train of thought here spoken of, more than any other thing, determines the character. Now it is by frequent or continued meditation upon a subject by placing a subject in different points of view, by dwelling upon proofs and consequences, that mental exercise is drawn into any particular channel. [And] I shall not, I believe, be contradicted when I say that if one train of thinking be more desirable than another, it is that which regards nature with a constant reference to a supreme, intelligent Author. Under this stupendous Being we live. Our happiness, our existence, is in His hands. All we expect must come from Him. Nor ought we to feel our situation insecure. In every nature, and in every portion of nature which we can descry, we find attention bestowed upon even the minutest arts. The hinges in the wing of an earwig and the joints of its antennae are as highly wrought as if the Creator had nothing else to finish. [And] we see no signs or dimunition of care by multiplicity of objects, or of distraction of thought by variety. We have no reason to fear, therefore, our being forgotten, or overlooked, or neglected.

The existence and character of the Deity is, in every view, the most interesting of all human speculations. In none, however, is it more so than as it facilitates the belief of the fundamental articles of revelation. It is a step to have it proved that there must be something in the world more than what we see. It is a further step to know that, amongst the visible things of nature, there must be an intelligent mind concerned in its production, order and support. These points being assured to us by *natural* theology, we may leave to revelation the disclosure of particulars which our researches cannot reach, respecting either the nature of this Being as the original Cause of all things, or of His character and designs as a moral governor.

The true theist will be the first to listen to *any* credible communication of Divine knowledge. Nothing which he has learned from natural theology will diminish his desire of further instruction or his disposition to receive it with humility and thankfulness. He wishes for light. He rejoices in light. His inward veneration of this great Being will incline him to attend with the utmost seriousness not only to all that can be discovered concerning Him by researches into nature, but to all that is taught by a revelation which gives reasonable proof of having proceeded from Him.

But, above every other article of revealed religion, does the belief of a Deity bear with the strongest force upon that grand point which gives importance to all the rest – the resurrection of the dead. The thing might appear hopeless did we not see a Power at work adequate to the effect, a Power under the guidance of an intelligent Will, and a Power penetrating the inmost recesses of all substance. I am far from justifying the opinion of those who thought it a thing incredible that God should raise the dead. But I admit that it is first necessary to be persuaded that there is a God to do so! This [much] being thoroughly settled in our minds, there seems to be nothing in this process (concealed as we confess it to be) which need shock our belief. In everything which respects this change, we have a wise and powerful Being upon Whom to rely for the execution of any plan which His goodness or His justice may have formed. That great office rests with Him. Be it ours to hope, under a firm and settled persuasion, that, living and dying, we are His.

Finis

What the CSM is all about

The **Creation Science Movement** started in 1932 protesting about the influence of Darwin's theory of evolution. It was called the Evolution Protest Movement (EPM) in those days.

The prime movers were Mr Douglas Dewar, barrister and Auditor General of the Indian Civil Service, and Captain Bernard Acworth DSO, who developed the asdic sonar device (Who's Who). They called the first meeting of the EPM at 21 Essex Gardens, The Strand, London, in 1932. The first public meeting was reported in *The Times* on February 12, 1935. Sir Ambrose Fleming presided and what he said then still stands for what the Creation Science Movement believes in today.

He declared that

'of late years the Darwinian anthropology had been forced on public attention by numerous books ... in such a fashion as to create a belief that it was a certainly settled scientific truth. The fact that many eminent naturalists did not agree that Darwin's theory of species production had been sufficiently established as a truth was generally repressed. If there had been no creation, there was no need to assume any Creator; the chief basis for all religion was taken away and morality reduced to mere human expediency. It had seemed to a large number of thoughtful persons that it was of national importance to ... counteract the effects of reckless and indiscriminate popularisation of the theory of the wholly animal origin of mankind, especially among the young, by the diffusion of a truly scientific ... cause for all those altruistic, aesthetic, intellectual, spiritual and religious faculties ... in man, of which not the very slightest trace was seen in the animal species ... they desired to oppose a one-sided materialistic presentation of human origin which rejected altogether any suggestion of creation ... They said that the arguments of the Darwinian anthropologists were defective in logic and did not give the proof they assumed.'

This was reported over half a century ago! Today, society witnesses to the effect of atheistic humanism which belief in the theory of evolution has brought – fragmented family units, abortion, child abuse etc. In fact in all these intervening years the evidence has mounted up arguing that of course a Creator must have made this planet Earth and the heavens. There is a wealth of further scientific evidence supporting Creation which these eminent men in the early 1930s did not then know. Advances in our knowledge of genetics, biochemistry and information theory are just some areas where progress in the last sixty years has made belief in evolution even less logical.

The sense of high purpose expressed in *The Times* account is still what motivates CSM today. We are concerned that people today are rarely confronted with a straight-forward reading of the Bible starting at Genesis chapter one. In fact most people have been told that they cannot trust the beginning of God's Word. They rehearse Satan's own words, 'Hath God said?'. CSM declares that the doctrine of original sin is not based on myth or fable but rather on the solid foundation of the 'lively oracles' of the Lord God. A blurring of this truth affects the wonder of the Atonement by the peerless Son of God, which in turn can lead to a shallow commitment to Him. CSM ringingly declares that the beginning of God's Word may be trusted as well as all that follows.

What else does CSM do? A pamphlet on different subjects giving evidence of Creation is published every two months together with the *Creation Journal* which carries up-to-the-minute news and comment. These pamphlets form a valuable information resource on the Creation/evolution issue.

CSM provides able speakers on Creation who major on the scientific evidence which is increasingly weighty. Today many eminent scientists who do not even argue from the Christian standpoint, find this evidence against the theory of evolution sufficient to convince them that there is no evolution at all. This evidence is ignored in school textbooks and TV nature programmes. CSM lecturers regularly address universities, colleges, sixth forms and Church groups throughout the UK. In the 1960s our Creationist speakers toured the Far East, Australia, New Zealand and North America, while in the 1990s we are beginning to meet the need in Eastern Europe.

CSM has charitable status (Charity no: 801745). We are members of the Evangelical Alliance. May we admit that we need you as a member? The hard-nosed humanism of evolutionism has become entrenched in the British educational system and in society at large. We need your dedicated support to topple it! Your subscription will help; and if you could arrange a meeting as well, even better!

At heart CSM wishes to give glory to the Lord Jesus Christ who created man in the image of the Tri-une God, and then stooped to redeem us.

The address of the CSM is:

> Creation Science Movement
> 50 Brecon Avenue
> Cosham, Portsmouth
> PO6 2AW
> England